GRADE 4

Texas Treasures

Practice Book

Macmillan/McGraw-Hill

B

The *McGraw·Hill* Companies

 Macmillan/McGraw-Hill

Published by Macmillan/McGraw-Hill, of McGraw-Hill Education, a division of The McGraw-Hill Companies, Inc.,
Two Penn Plaza, New York, New York 10121.

Printed in the United States of America

6 7 8 9 HSO 14 13 12 11 10

Contents

Unit 1 • Growing Up

Contents

Unit 2 • Making a Difference

Contents

Unit 3 • The Power of Words

Contents

Unit 4 • Working Together

Contents

Unit 5 • Habitats

Contents

Unit 6 • Problem Solving

Name _____

Each vowel has a long and a short sound. The **short vowel sounds** are as follows:

a as in *flat*   *e* as in *shelf*   *i* as in *mill*   *o* as in *blot*   *u* as in *sum*

When a vowel comes between two consonants, it usually has a short sound.

A. Read the sentences below. Circle each word that has a short vowel sound between two consonants.

1. The police found the cash behind the shelf.

2. One thief ran to the dock.

3. One thief had a plot to steal the bell.

4. The thieves hid behind a big tree.

5. They lay flat on the grass.

B. Circle the words with short vowel sounds. Then use three of them in sentences.

plate   left   bleat   cove   load   mill   past   neat   leave   crunch   plum

6. _____

_____

7. _____

_____

8. _____

_____

Name _____

| opportunities | boycotts | citizen |
| unions | strikes | border |

A. Choose the correct word from the box to complete each sentence.

1. Sometimes workers go on _____ to demand higher pay.

2. In America, a _____ can vote to choose leaders in the government.

3. Some workers join _____ with other people who do the same job.

4. Mexico shares a _____ with the United States.

5. People move from one country to another for different reasons, but all of

   them are looking for _____ to better their lives.

6. People will sometimes start _____ against companies and refuse to buy things from them.

B. Write sentences using three of the vocabulary words.

7. _____

8. _____

9. _____

TEKS **4.2 (B)** Use the context of the sentence to determine the meaning of unfamiliar words.

Name _____

Authors may not tell you everything about the characters and events in a story. However, you need the information to understand the characters. You can use clues from the text to **make inferences**.

Sheila hopped and skipped to school. Today was the first day of school.

You know that Sheila is happy because she is hopping and skipping.

The yellow bus picked Xian up at the corner. He did not know anyone on the bus. He sat next to a girl in a red sweater. "Hi," she smiled. Xian knew the word and said *hi* back. "My name's Nancy." Xian just looked at her.

"Do you have Mr. Bellino this year?" Xian said nothing. "You're new, aren't you?" Xian bit his lip and stared at Nancy.

When the bus stopped, Nancy led Xian up the walk. "I'll show you around." Xian had a friend, and he gave Nancy a big smile.

Use the passage to answer the questions.

1. Why doesn't Xian answer some of Nancy's questions?

_____

2. What clues tell you that Xian needs help from Nancy?

_____

3. Why does Nancy offer to lead Xian up the walk?

_____

4. How does Xian feel at the end of the passage? How do you know?

_____

TEKS 4.6 (B) Describe the interaction of characters including their relationships and the changes they undergo.

Name _____

As you read *My Diary from Here to There*, fill in the Inferences Web.

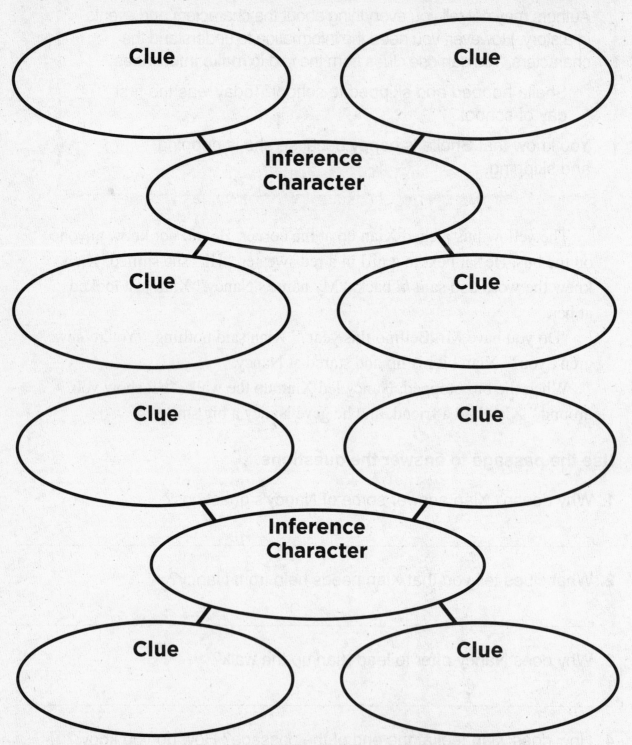

How does the information you wrote in the Inferences Web help you understand the main character in *My Diary from Here to There*?

TEKS 4.6 (B) Describe the interaction of characters including their relationships and the changes they undergo.

Name _____

As I read, I will pay attention to my intonation and expression.

	Paolo stood on the deck of the steamship SS *Laconia*,
10	which was anchored in New York Harbor. He was trying
20	to see the island, but it was covered with morning mist.
31	It almost seemed dangerous, lurking in the water like a sea
42	monster. Paolo was very nervous, and the worst part was he
53	didn't know why.
56	Paolo coughed. His cough was getting worse. It was
65	the air down in steerage, he thought. Deep down in the
76	ship was a large, open area filled with bunk beds. It was
88	called steerage. Paolo and his parents had spent the trip
98	from Italy in this big room. It was crowded with
108	immigrants who couldn't afford the expensive tickets.
115	Paolo went up on deck to get a breath of air whenever he
128	could. The air blowing in from the ocean was a relief. 139

Comprehension Check

1. What is Paolo doing on the steamship in the beginning? **Plot**

2. Why might Paolo be nervous? **Plot**

	Words Read	–	Number of Errors	=	Words Correct Score
First Read		–		=	
Second Read		–		=	

© Macmillan/McGraw-Hill

TEKS 4.1 Read aloud grade-level stories with fluency and comprehension.

My Diary from Here to There
Grade 4/Unit 1

5

Name _____

When you **monitor and adjust comprehension**, you check that you understand what you are reading. One way to do this is to connect your experience and **background knowledge** to the story. Another way is to **ask and answer questions** about the selection. A third strategy is to **reread** a portion of the text aloud.

Read the story below. Then complete the items that follow.

Matt sadly watched the moving truck drive away. His friends back in Dallas would be at school the next day without him. Matt wondered whom his best friend would eat with at lunch. Then he thought, "Who will eat lunch with *me* at my new school? I don't know anyone in San Antonio."

Matt saw his basketball on top of an open box. He put up a shot. The ball sailed through the net. "Not bad," said a voice from behind him. Matt turned around. A boy about his own age stood there. "My name is Josh," he said. "I live across the street. Can I play?" Matt smiled and bounced Josh the ball.

1. Think about a time when you had to make a change. Connect your experience to the way that Matt feels in the story.

   _____

   _____

2. Ask and answer a literal question about what happens in the story.

   _____

   _____

3. Ask and answer an interpretive question about Matt's or Josh's feelings in

   the story. _____

   _____

4. Ask and answer an evaluative question about the way that the author ends the story.

   _____

   _____

TEKS RC-4 (B) Ask literal, interpretive, and evaluative questions of text.
RC-4 (C) Monitor and adjust comprehension.

© Macmillan/McGraw-Hill

A **time line** is a visual way to show a sequence of events in a period of time. Events that happened during that time period are placed on the time line in the order in which they happened.

Statehood Time Line

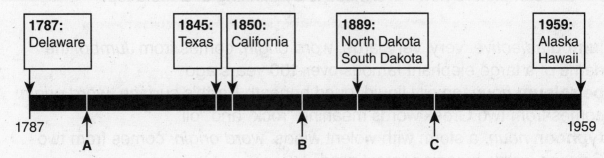

| 1787: Delaware | | 1845: Texas | 1850: California | | 1889: North Dakota South Dakota | | 1959: Alaska Hawaii |

1787   1959
        A   B   C

Use the time line to answer the questions.

1. What is the subject of this time line?

   _____

   _____

2. When did Texas become a state? _____

3. Which states became states in 1889? _____

   _____

4. How many years does the time line cover? _____

5. Arizona and New Mexico became states in 1912. Where would you put

   that event on the time line: at point A, point B, or point C? _____

6. What is the earliest date on this time line? The latest date? _____

Name _____

A dictionary sometimes tells you where a word comes from.
Knowing the **origin** of a word can help you understand it.
  mesa *noun.* a hill or mountain with a flat top
  word origin: In Spanish the word *mesa* means "table."
How does the origin help you understand the word?
You can picture how flat a mesa is by thinking of a table top.

jumbo *adjective.* very, very large. *word origin:* comes from *Jumbo*, the name of a large elephant famous over 100 years ago
petroleum *noun.* an oily liquid found beneath Earth's surface. *word origin:* comes from two Greek words meaning "rock" and "oil"
typhoon *noun.* a storm with violent winds. *word origin:* comes from two Chinese words meaning "great wind"
zero *noun.* the number 0, which means no amount at all. *word origin:* comes from an Arabic word that means "empty"

Use the dictionary entries above to answer the questions.

1. How does the word origin of *jumbo* help you understand the word?

_____

_____

2. How does the word origin of *typhoon* help you understand the word?

_____

3. How does the word origin of *petroleum* help you understand the word?

_____

_____

4. How does the word origin of *zero* help you understand the word?

_____

_____

© Macmillan/McGraw-Hill

TEKS **4.2 (A)** Determine the meaning of grade-level academic English words derived from Greek and other linguistic roots.

Name _____

A. Reading Strategy: Set a Purpose for Reading

As you read, think about your purpose for reading. You might set your own purpose for reading, or your teacher might set a purpose for you. Choose a text that you will read this week, and complete the activity.

Before Reading Circle the phrase that best completes the statement.

My purpose is to . . .

be entertained.   think about life or how
                                         people act.

learn about something.   find out how to do
                                         something.

form an opinion about   make a decision about
something.   something.

After Reading Complete the statement.

Because I read to _____, I better understood _____.

B. Independent Reading Log

Choose something you would like to read. After reading, complete the reading log. Be sure to paraphrase, or tell the main idea or meaning of the text. Keep the details or events in the correct order. You may use the log to talk to others about what you read.

Genre _____

Title _____

Author _____

This Text Is About _____

_____

_____

_____

_____

_____

TEKS **4.9** Read independently for a sustained period of time and paraphrase what the reading was about, maintaining meaning and logical order. **RC-4 (A)** Establish purposes for reading selected texts based upon own or others' desired outcome to enhance comprehension.

My Diary from Here to There
Grade 4/Unit I   9

Name _____

The long *a* sound can be spelled the following ways:
ay tod<u>ay</u>, str<u>ay</u>   **ai** r<u>ai</u>l, dr<u>ai</u>n   **a_e** sl<u>a</u>t<u>e</u>, gr<u>a</u>z<u>e</u>
ei n<u>ei</u>gh, sl<u>ei</u>gh   **ea** br<u>ea</u>k, gr<u>ea</u>t

Read the following sentences. Write the words in the sentences that have a long *a* sound on the lines below.

1. The baby wood rats played outside today.

_____

2. Does it take long to make a crate for a rattlesnake?

_____

3. Rain in the desert can cause a great flood.

_____

4. Desert sunsets paint the sky bright colors.

_____

5. Did you see the snake that just slithered across the trail?

_____

6. Don't break away from the trail when walking in the desert.

_____

7. We heard the stray horses neigh as they grazed on desert bushes.

_____

8. We hiked in the desert until my legs ached and I felt faint.

_____

TEKS 3.1 (E) Monitor accuracy in decoding.

Name _____

| curious | policy | ranged |
| temporary | several | frequently |

**Write a complete sentence to answer each question below.
In your answer, use the vocabulary word in bold type.**

1. What is something you can do today, but couldn't do **several** years ago?

_____

2. What do you think is a good **policy** for people to follow?

_____

3. What is something that **frequently** happens at surprise parties?

_____

4. What is something that would make you **curious**?

_____

5. If you had a pet toad, what would make a good **temporary** home for it?

_____

6. What happened on a day when your emotions **ranged** from bored to excited?

_____

Now use one of the words above in a sentence of your own.

7. _____

TEKS **4.2 (B)** Use the context of the sentence to determine the meaning of
unfamiliar words.

> Every story has story elements. The **characters** are the people or animals in a story. The **setting** is where and when a story takes place. The **plot** is what happens in the story.

Read the passage below. Underline the answers in the passage and then write the answers.

Nadia was in her bedroom. Although it was her birthday, she wasn't happy. Her best friend, Molly, had moved away, and this would be her first birthday without her. She didn't feel like celebrating her birthday this year.

Her dad came in and told her not to come into the backyard until 3 o'clock. Nadia knew that her family was busy setting up for the party.

At 3 o'clock, Nadia walked into the backyard. She saw balloons, a birthday cake, and some friends. Then she noticed a huge carton. Her dad told her to open it right away. She opened the box and out jumped Molly!

Who are the main characters in the story?

1. _____   2. _____

Where does the beginning of the story take place?

3. _____

What is the main character's problem?

4. _____

_____

Sequence and summarize the plot of the story.

5. _____

_____

© Macmillan/McGraw-Hill

TEKS 4.6 (A) Sequence and summarize the plot's main events.

Name _____

As you read *The Adventures of Ali Baba Bernstein*, fill in the
Story Flowchart.

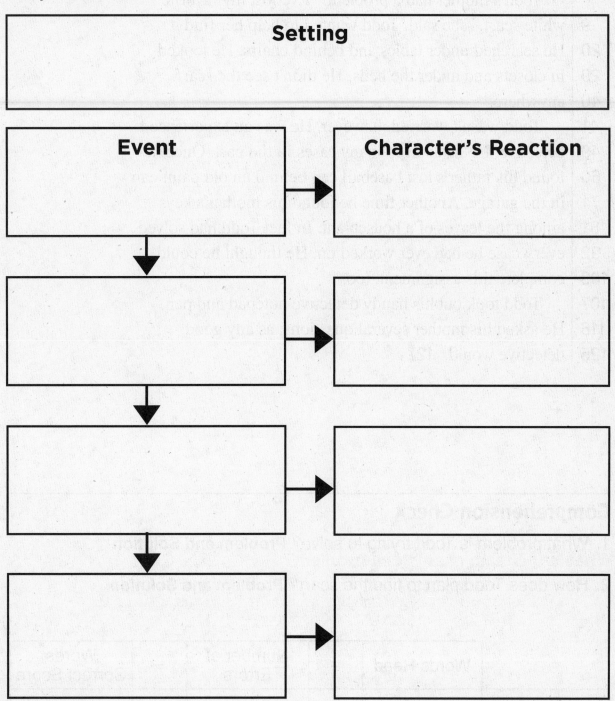

Setting

Event   **Character's Reaction**

How does the information you wrote in this chart help you understand
The Adventures of Ali Baba Bernstein?

TEKS 4.6 (A) Sequence and summarize the plot's main events.

Name _____

As I read, I will focus on reading accurately.

	Todd's mother had a problem. "I've lost my favorite
9	white scarf," she said. Todd wanted to help her find it.
20	He searched under tables and behind chairs. He looked
29	in closets and under the beds. He didn't see the scarf
40	anywhere.
41	Todd wasn't worried, however. He was an experienced
49	detective. He had solved many cases in the past. Once he
60	found his father's lost baseball cap behind an old paint can
71	in the garage. Another time he found his mother's keys
81	among the leaves of a houseplant. In fact Todd had solved
92	every case he had ever worked on. He thought he could
103	complete this assignment, too.
107	Todd took out his handy detective notepad and pen.
116	He asked his mother several questions, as any good
125	detective would. 127

Comprehension Check

1. What problem is Todd trying to solve? **Problem and Solution**

2. How does Todd plan to find the scarf? **Problem and Solution**

	Words Read	–	Number of Errors	=	Words Correct Score
First Read		–		=	
Second Read		–		=	

© Macmillan/McGraw-Hill

TEKS 4.1 Read aloud grade-level stories with fluency and comprehension.

Writers include **maps** to show readers geographic locations
and physical features, such as mountains and seas.

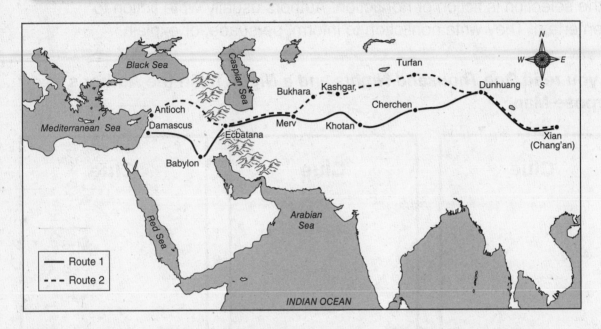

Use the map of the Silk Routes to answer the questions below.

1. If a traveler began in Xian, what towns would he pass through on Silk

   Route 1 before reaching Merv? _____

2. Name three bodies of water shown on this map. _____

   _____

3. In what general direction would a traveler need to go to travel from

   Kashgar to Turfan? _____

4. What city on the Silk Routes is nearest to the Caspian Sea?

   _____

TEKS 4.13 (B) Explain factual information presented graphically.

When you **compare** two or more things, you are looking for how they are similar. When you **contrast** two or more things, you are looking for how they are different. Sometimes authors use an explicit comparison-contrast text structure and include signal words.

Words that Signal a Comparison		
alike	each	similar
also	in addition to	too
both	same	

Words that Signal a Contrast		
different	in contrast	separately
but	while	opposite
on the other hand	instead	
however	separate	

Write whether you think each sentence below is part of a *comparison* or a *contrast*. Circle the word or words that you base your answer on.

1. Jennifer and Jeffrey were twins, but they had very different ideas about how to run a business. _____

2. Monique's second business was also quite successful. _____

3. Both of the students have their own business. _____

4. The first job David had was boring; on the other hand, his second job was interesting. _____

5. Walking dogs was fun, while mowing lawns was hard. _____

6. Keisha liked spending; however, Julie wanted to save. _____

7. Sandy and Pedro mowed lawns and were alike in the way they treated their customers. _____

TEKS 4.11 (C) Describe explicit relationships among ideas in texts organized by comparison.

Kid Reporters at Work
Grade 4/Unit 1
21

As you read *Kid Reporters at Work,* **fill in the Venn diagram.**

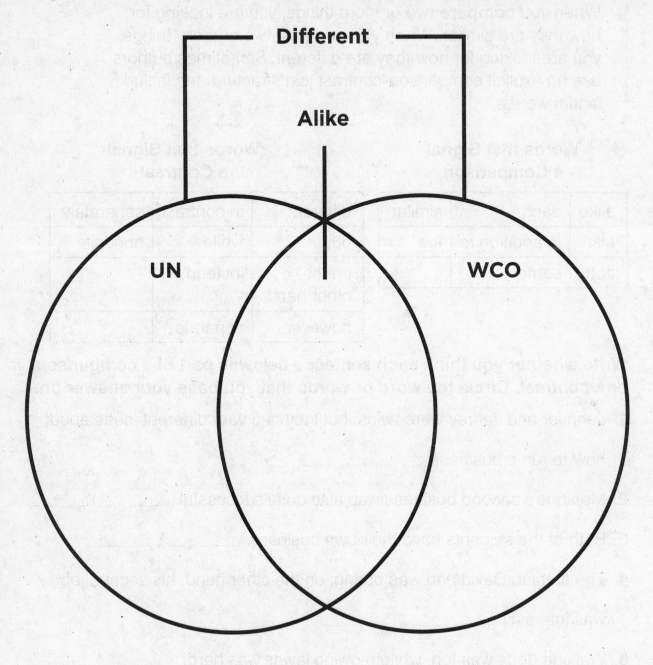

Different

Alike

UN

WCO

How does the information you wrote in the Venn diagram help you
understand how the author organized ideas in *Kid Reporters at Work*?

TEKS **4.11 (C)** Describe explicit relationships among ideas in texts organized
by comparison.

22 Kid Reporters at Work
Grade 4/Unit I

As I read, I will pay attention to my intonation and rate.

	Everyone needs money, even kids. Some kids get
8	allowances. And some **enterprising** kids work to earn extra
17	money. They have paper routes or run lemonade stands.
26	They shovel snow or mow grass. They baby-sit or pet-sit.
36	You may do these things yourself.
42	But some kids have jobs that are special. They are
52	dream jobs. These jobs are hard to get. They are so good
64	that you might do them for free!
71	If you love baseball, your dream job might be working
81	as a bat boy or girl. If you love performing, your dream job
94	might be working as an actor.
100	Why are dream jobs so hard to get? To begin with, there
112	aren't many of these jobs. And there are many children
122	who want them. Laws also limit when, where, and how
132	many hours children can work. That's good. In the 1800s,
141	kids often worked instead of going to school. Those kids
151	had hard lives. Laws make sure that can't happen now. 161

Comprehension Check

1. How are dream jobs different from ordinary jobs? In which ways are they alike? **Compare and Contrast**

2. Name the main idea and supporting details in the last paragraph. **Main Idea and Details**

	Words Read	–	Number of Errors	=	Words Correct Score
First Read		–		=	
Second Read		–		=	

TEKS 4.1 Read aloud grade-level stories with fluency and comprehension.

Kid Reporters at Work **23**
Grade 4/Unit 1

A **guide word** appears at the top of each page in an encyclopedia. To locate information, look at the guide words. The word on the left page is the first topic, or entry, shown on that page. The word on the right page is the last entry shown on that page.

An encyclopedia entry contains a **topic sentence**. The topic sentence gives you an overview of the entry. Each entry also has a **concluding sentence**. This sentence often gives a final detail.

Look at the encyclopedia pages. Then answer the questions.

368 **Orange**		**Orchestra** 369	
orange, *OR anj,* is a popular fruit throughout the world. It is known for its juice and contains many	vitamins and minerals. Oranges grow in countries such as Brazil and the United States. People have grown	oranges for thousands of years. Today, most oranges are grown to make juice, but they are used in	other products, too. There are many types of oranges, and all grow in warm climates.

1. What are the guide words on these encyclopedia pages? Circle them.

2. According to the guide words, which entry would you find on pages 368–369?

   A. orchid   C. organ

   B. orbit   D. Oregon

3. According to the topic sentence, what is the entry going to be about?

   _____

4. What information does the concluding sentence tell you?

   _____

   _____

© Macmillan/McGraw-Hill

TEKS 4.11 **(D)** Use multiple text features to gain an overview of the contents of text and to locate information.

You can use the library to collect information from multiple sources, including books written by experts, reference texts, and online searches. You can search for a book in a library's **electronic card catalog** by **subject**, **author**, or **title**. The books will show up in a screen that looks like this.

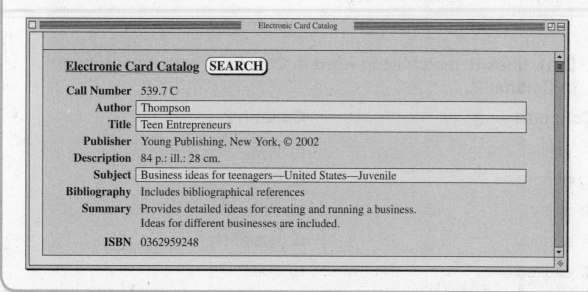

A. Circle the correct information from the card-catalog card above.

1. The title of the book is:

Young Publishing   Teen Entrepreneurs

2. The author of the book is:

Thompson   Young

3. In what year was the book published?

539.7 C   2002

B. Read the summary on the card to answer the question.

4. Would this book help you find ideas for classroom projects? Why?

_____

TEKS 4.24 (A) (ii) Collect information from multiple sources, including data from experts, reference texts, and online searches.

Kid Reporters at Work   **25**
Grade 4/Unit I

Name _____

> Words that have opposite meanings are called **antonyms**.
> A word can have more than one antonym.
>
> | Word | Antonyms |
> |------|----------|
> | glad | sad, unhappy |
> | angry | calm, pleased |

A. Draw lines to match each word in Column 1 with an antonym in Column 2.

Column 1	Column 2
1. selfish	**a.** full
2. hungry	**b.** calm
3. noisy	**c.** slow
4. speedy	**d.** unselfish
5. excited	**e.** quiet

B. In the blank, write an antonym for each underlined word.

6. My dad was <u>happy</u> _____ when he saw my report card.

7. The fabric of the cushion felt very <u>smooth</u> _____.

8. The light in the room was <u>dim</u> _____.

9. Thalia made a fruit salad with cherries that were so <u>sweet</u>

_____.

10. I looked out the window and saw <u>sunny</u> _____ weather.

© Macmillan/McGraw-Hill

TEKS 3.4 (C) Identify and use antonyms.

A. Reading Strategy: Set a Purpose for Reading

As you read, think about your purpose for reading. You might set your own purpose for reading, or your teacher might set a purpose for you. Choose a text that you will read this week, and answer the questions.

What is the title? _____

What is the subject? _____

What do you already know or think about this subject? _____

_____

_____

What do you want to know about this subject? _____

_____

_____

_____

What is your purpose for reading this text? _____

B. Independent Reading Log

Choose something you would like to read. After reading, complete the reading log. Be sure to paraphrase, or tell the main idea or meaning of the text. Keep the details or events in the correct order. You may use the log to talk to others about what you read.

Genre _____

Title _____

Author _____

This Text Is About _____

_____

_____

_____

_____

TEKS **4.9** Read independently for a sustained period of time and paraphrase what the reading was about, maintaining meaning and logical order. **RC-4 (A)** Establish purposes for reading selected texts based upon own or others' desired outcome to enhance comprehension.

Kid Reporters at Work
Grade 4/Unit I **27**

> Remember the following common spellings for the **long *i***
> **sound:** *ie, i-e, igh, i,* and *y*.

A. Complete the following sentences with one of these long *i* words.

> | | | | | | | |
> |---|---|---|---|---|---|---|
> | kind | drive | kite | wipe | pride | sky | prime |
> | sly | sigh | fright | pies | spy | twice | find |

1. The rocket rose up into the _____.

2. What _____ of person becomes an astronaut?

3. Fernando went outside on a windy day to fly his _____.

4. The spaceship orbited the moon not once, but _____.

5. The astronauts wanted to _____ life on Mars.

6. It's much easier to _____ a car than to pilot a spaceship.

B. Circle the word in each pair that has the long *i* sound.

7. fit   fight

8. dine   done

9. fleas   flies

10. rip   ripe

11. trim   try

12. high   hog

TEKS 3.1 (E) Monitor accuracy in decoding.

| endless | display | protested |
| sensible | paralyzed | realistic |

A. Replace the underlined word(s) with one of the words from the vocabulary list.

1. I <u>complained about</u> traveling alone. _____

2. A trip in space may seem <u>without a finish</u>. _____

3. The film about space travel was <u>the way things are</u>. _____

4. His plan for launching a rocket was not <u>well thought-out</u>.

   _____

5. The astronaut seemed <u>unable to move</u> when he climbed outside the

   spaceship. _____

B. Use three of the vocabulary words in sentences of your own.

6. _____

   _____

7. _____

   _____

8. _____

   _____

TEKS 4.2 (B) Use the context of the sentence to determine the meaning of unfamiliar words.

The Astronaut and the Onion
Grade 4/Unit 1   29

Name _____

Analyzing a story can help you describe and understand the interaction between **characters**, their relationships, and the changes the characters undergo.

Read the passage. Then answer the questions that follow.

When she was little, Andrea lived near the Kennedy Space Center. Her mother always took her there to watch the rockets launch. As Andrea grew up, she realized that she wanted to do more than just watch rocket launches. More than anything, she wanted to be an astronaut, but she wasn't sure that she could be one.

Her mother told her, "If you want something, the important thing is that you try your best." Andrea ate well and exercised. She studied hard in all her subjects. After college she learned to fly jet planes.

Andrea's dream came true. She became an astronaut and took many trips into space.

1. Who are the characters in this story?

_____

2. What did Andrea want to be when she grew up?

_____

3. How did Andrea's mother help Andrea achieve her goal?

_____

4. In most plots, a character changes. How did Andrea change in the story?

_____

_____

TEKS 4.6 (B) Describe the interaction of characters including their relationships and the changes they undergo.

Name _____

As you read *The Astronaut and the Onion*, fill in the Character Web.

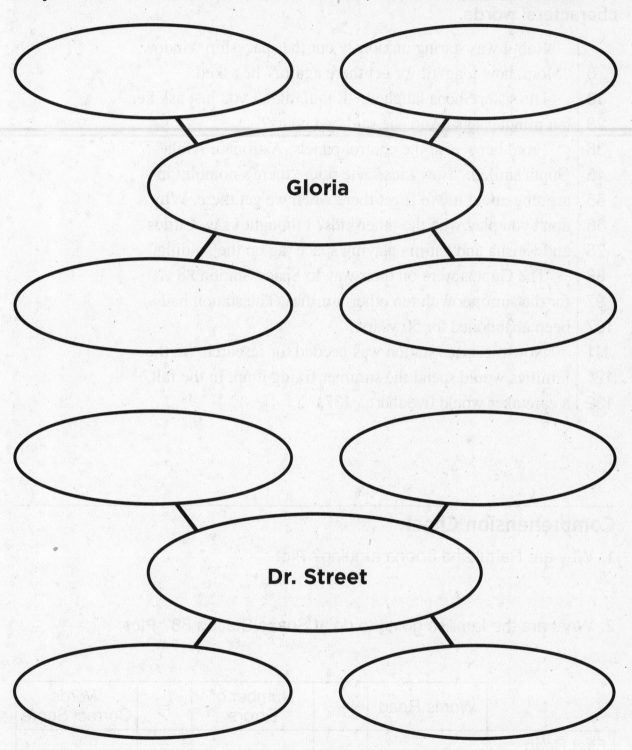

Gloria

Dr. Street

How does the information you wrote in the Character Web help you summarize *The Astronaut and the Onion*?

TEKS 4.6 (B) Describe the interaction of characters including their relationships.

The Astronaut and the Onion
Grade 4/Unit I   3I

© Macmillan/McGraw-Hill

As I read, I will pay attention to pauses, stops, and the characters' words.

	Rahul was staring anxiously out the spaceship window.
8	"Mom, how long 'til we get there again?" he asked.
18	His sister Shona laughed. "Rahul, didn't you just ask her
28	ten minutes ago? And she said two hours?"
36	From her seat at the control panels, Astronaut Amla
45	Gupta smiled. "Now kids," she said, "there's no point in
55	arguing about it. We'll get there when we get there. Why
66	don't you play with the other kids? I thought I saw Carlos
78	and Keisha and Fatima playing space tag on the landing."
88	The Guptas were on their way to Space Station 88
97	for the summer with ten other families. The station had
107	been abandoned for 50 years.
111	Now the space station was needed for research. So the
121	families would spend the summer fixing it up. In the fall,
132	a caretaker would live there. 137

Comprehension Check

1. Why are Rahul and Shona arguing? **Plot**

2. What are the families going to do at Space Station 88? **Plot**

	Words Read	−	Number of Errors	=	Words Correct Score
First Read		−		=	
Second Read		−		=	

© Macmillan/McGraw-Hill

TEKS 4.1 Read aloud grade-level stories with fluency and comprehension.

> The **narrator** is the person who tells the story. Sometimes the narrator is a character in the story and uses the pronoun *I* to tell the story. This type of narrator tells the story from a **first-person** point of view. Sometimes the narrator is not a character in the story and refers to the characters by name or as *he* or *she*. This type of narrator tells the story from a **third-person** point of view.

Read each passage. Then answer the questions below.

1.   I looked at the glowing red numbers beside my bed. Oh no! I had slept late again. I grabbed clothes without thinking. I stopped in the kitchen for fruit and a bottle of juice. At the last second I remembered to grab my bag. I ran down the block to the bus stop. I could see the other kids piling into the bus. I made it just as the driver was closing the doors. He smiled at me.

    "Just in time," he said.

2.   Enrique had a hard time waking up in the mornings. His mom warned him, "Enrique, no matter what, do not miss that bus again!"

    Enrique woke up and saw that he had slept late again. He jumped out of bed. He grabbed a quick breakfast and his bag. He ran for the bus. He could still see the bus. He knew that he had a chance! He got there as the driver was closing the door. The driver smiled at him.

    "Just in time," he said.

- What is the point of view of the first passage? How do you know?

_____

_____

- What is the point of view of the second passage? How do you know?

_____

_____

© Macmillan/McGraw-Hill

TEKS   **4.6 (C)**   Identify whether the narrator or speaker of a story is first or third person.

The Astronaut and the Onion
Grade 4/Unit 1

33

Directions explain how to do something. A **recipe** gives step-by-step directions for how to prepare a food. The steps are numbered to tell the reader the order in which things should be done. A list of ingredients usually begins the recipe.

Read the following recipe. Then answer the questions.

Fruit Salad

2 apples	**1 banana**	**¾ teaspoon ground cinnamon**
1 cup strawberries	**1 cup vanilla yogurt**	

1. Ask an adult to help you cut up the fruit.
2. Dice the apples.
3. Slice the banana and strawberries.
4. In a bowl, mix the diced apples, banana slices, and strawberry slices.
5. Fold in the yogurt.
6. Sprinkle the mixture with cinnamon and stir gently.

1. What fruit does the recipe call for?

_____

2. What is the first thing you do to make the fruit salad?

_____

3. When do you add yogurt to the salad?

_____

4. What is the last step in making the fruit salad?

_____

TEKS **4.13 (A)** Determine the sequence of activities needed to carry out a procedure.

Name _____

When you are reading and come to a word you do not know, a dictionary can tell you the word's meaning, pronunciation, and syllabication.

dis•tort (di stôrt´) *verb.* **1.** to twist the meaning of something. *The reporter* distorts *what people say.* **2.** to twist out of shape. *The mirror* distorts *my face when I look into it.*

A phonetic spelling tells you how to say the word. Notice that *distort* is divided into two parts. Each part is called a **syllable**.

The accent mark (´) after the second syllable shows you which syllable to stress when pronouncing the word.

Use the dictionary entry above to answer these questions.

1. Which meaning of *distort* do you find in the following sentence?

   Eduardo twisted the hanger and distorted its shape.

   a. Meaning #1   **b.** Meaning #2

2. True or false: *distort* has two syllables.

   a. true   **b.** false

3. Which is the correct way to say *distort*?

   a. di´ stôrt   **b.** di stôrt´

4. Use *distort* in a sentence of your own. Then write the number of the meaning you used.

   _____

   _____

   I used meaning # ____.

© Macmillan/McGraw-Hill

TEKS **4.2 (E)** Use a dictionary or glossary to determine the meanings, syllabication, and pronunciation of unknown words.

The Astronaut and the Onion **35**
Grade 4/Unit I

Name _____

A. Reading Strategy: Set a Purpose for Reading

As you read, think about your purpose for reading. You might set your own purpose for reading, or your teacher might set a purpose for you. Choose a text that you will read this week, and complete the activity.

Look at the title. What do you think the text will be about? _____

_____

_____

Look at any pictures or photographs that go with the text. What do they tell you about the subject? _____

_____

_____

Read the first paragraph. Why do you think the author wrote the text?

_____

_____

_____

Think about your answers to the first three questions. What is your purpose for reading this text? _____

B. Independent Reading Log

Choose something you would like to read. After reading, complete the reading log. Be sure to paraphrase, or tell the main idea or meaning of the text. Keep the details or events in the correct order. You may use the log to talk to others about what you read.

Genre _____

Title _____

Author _____

This Text Is About _____

_____

_____

36 The Astronaut and the Onion
Grade 4/Unit 1

TEKS **4.9** Read independently for a sustained period of time and paraphrase what the reading was about, maintaining meaning and logical order. **RC-4 (A)** Establish purposes for reading selected texts based upon own or others' desired outcome to enhance comprehension.

Name _____

The long **o** sound can be spelled several different ways.
st<u>o</u>l<u>e</u> (o_e)   f<u>oa</u>m (oa)   fl<u>ow</u> (ow)   m<u>o</u>ld (o)

Fill in the blanks using each long o word in the box once.

boat	close	floating	shallow	know
most	don't	home	soaked	go
rowed	owned	Cole	foal	hoped

1. We were _____ in our _____.

2. Along the bank we saw the _____ beautiful white horse.

3. I asked _____ if he knew who _____ her.

4. He answered, "I _____ _____."

5. Just then I caught sight of something small and brown and whispered,

   "She has a _____!"

6. "How _____ do you think we can get?" I asked.

7. I _____ to feed them the leftover apples from our lunch.

8. We _____ until the bottom scuffed against something

   below us, and I stepped out to wade through the _____
   water to the shore.

9. To my surprise I promptly sank instead. I got _____!
   Cole thought it was hysterical!

10. "Let's _____ _____," I grumbled.

Name _____

aware   selecting   positive   consisted   peculiar   advanced

A. Complete each sentence with a word from the box.

1. As the sound grew louder, Connie became _____ that a train was coming.

2. Ted had trouble _____ a different book because he liked to read only mysteries.

3. "You have a _____ taste in music," Tobie told Andre. "I never thought I would meet a nine-year-old who liked Bach."

4. Andre's choices at the library always _____ of history books about the period too.

5. "I am absolutely _____ that you will love this book about horses," Laura assured Marie.

6. Both girls then argued over which of the two was the more _____ reader.

B. Write a sentence using the word listed.

7. peculiar _____

_____

8. selecting _____

_____

C. Write a definition of the listed word, using your own words.

9. advanced _____

_____

TEKS **4.2 (B)** Use the context of the sentence to determine the meaning of unfamiliar words.

Name _____

> **Sequence** is the order in which events happen in a story. To list events in sequence, look for key words like *first*, *then*, and *last*.

Read the passage below. Then answer the questions that follow.

It was our town's worst storm. The next morning we saw our library had been struck by lightning and then caught fire. After seeing my favorite building in ruins, I decided something needed to be done.

First, I wrote a letter to our town's mayor. I emphasized the importance of having a library and why we needed to rebuild. Then, I decided to raise money. I asked some friends to help. Together, we baked cupcakes, washed cars, and collected money. I even got people to sign a petition—a piece of paper asking for something—saying that we needed to build a new library.

Finally, I took all the money we had raised along with the petition to the mayor's office. It turned out that the mayor had already been busy trying to design a new library. He was really impressed with all the work I had done and asked me to continue raising money for the new library!

1. What was the first thing that happened to the public library? How do you know? _____

_____

2. What was the first thing the narrator did? What was the second thing?

_____

_____

3. What was the last thing the narrator did for the library? _____

_____

_____

TEKS 4.6 (A) Sequence the plot's main events.

As you read *Because of Winn-Dixie*, fill in the Sequence Chart.

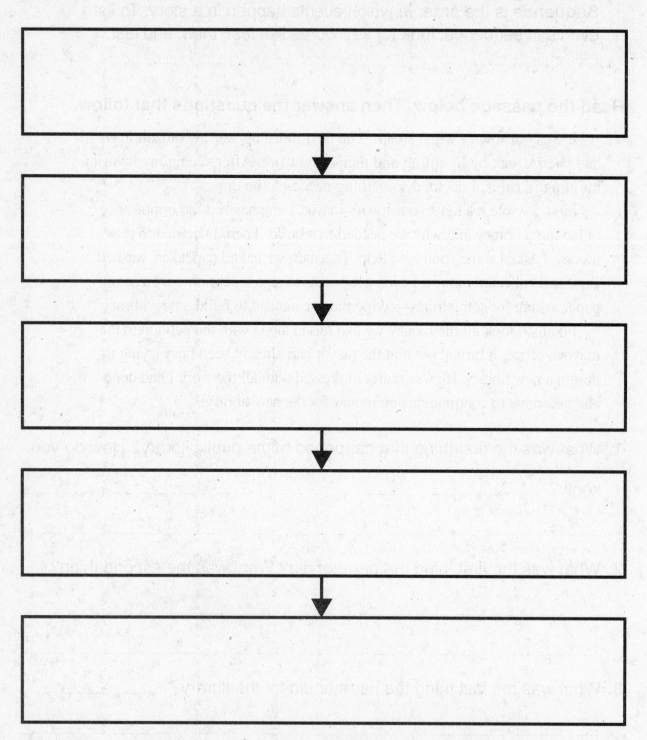

How does the information you wrote in the Sequence Chart help you
summarize *Because of Winn-Dixie*?

TEKS 4.6 (A) Sequence and summarize the plot's main events.

As I read, I will pay attention to end punctuation.

	Nate Jasper fumbled for his library card and handed it
10	to Ms. Kim, the librarian. He was checking out books
20	about life in the American colonies for a social studies
30	report. He hadn't realized it was his turn because he
40	was distracted by a sign taped to the wall beside the
51	circulation desk.
53	The sign read: "First Annual Highland Drawing
60	Contest. Prizes to be awarded for drawings that best show
70	the exciting and unique beauty of Highland, Vermont."
78	"I see that our drawing contest has caught your eye,"
88	said Ms. Kim. "Are you an artist?"
95	"Yeah, I guess I am," said Nate. "But I've never entered
106	a contest."
108	"Well, why not consider making this your first?" asked
117	Ms. Kim. "We have a Young Artists division, and we need
128	people like you to help make the contest a success. The
139	winning drawings will be displayed here in the Highland
148	Public Library. Here, take a flyer and think about it." 158

Comprehension Check

1. What does Ms. Kim say to Nate? **Plot**

2. Why is Nate a good candidate to enter the contest? **Character**

	Words Read	–	Number of Errors	=	Words Correct Score
First Read		–		=	
Second Read		–		=	

TEKS **4.1** Read aloud grade-level stories with fluency and comprehension.

Because of Winn-Dixie **41**
Grade 4/Unit 1

Authors use **sensory language**, such as metaphor and onomatopoeia, to create **imagery**, or pictures in the reader's mind. Sensory language helps readers see, hear, smell, taste, or feel something. **Onomatopoeia** is the use of a word that imitates the sound it stands for. *Buzz* is an example of onomatopoeia. A **metaphor** is a figure of speech in which two very different objects or ideas are said to be alike. *You are my sunshine* is a metaphor.

Read the poem. Then answer the questions below.

The Garden

The garden is my secret world.
I enter and am carried away.
The wind whispers softly.
The flowers dance and play.
Dew drip, drip, drips from the leaves.

I stand so still that I am a statue.
The garden comes to life around me.
Red tulips drink tea with pink roses.
The butterfly plays tag with the bee.
The oak tree hum, hum, hums a happy tune.

1. Which word in the fifth line is an example of onomatopoeia?

_____

2. Write the two metaphors that appear in the poem.

_____

3. What two things are compared in each metaphor?

_____

_____

© Macmillan/McGraw-Hill

TEKS 4.8 Identify the author's use of metaphors to produce imagery.

Name _____

> A **free verse poem** usually does not rhyme.
> A **stanza** is a group of lines that give the poem its form.
> A **line break** is the place in the poem where the line ends.
> A **simile** compares two different things using *like* or *as*.

Read the poem below. Then answer the questions that follow.

Books

What can you do with books, anyway?
You can laugh at them,
   frown at them, slam them shut.
You can stack them cover to cover
   till they're as tall as a skyscraper.
You can stuff them in your backpack
   till it's heavy like an elephant.
Or you can take one, crack it open,
   and read.

1. Why do you think the poet wrote this poem in one stanza?

_____

2. Write the two similes that appear in the poem.

_____

_____

3. What two things are being compared in the similes you wrote above?

_____

_____

4. Why did the poet write "and read" on a line by itself?

_____

TEKS 4.4 Explain how the structural elements of poetry relate to form.

The dictionary definition of a word is its **denotation.**
The feelings associated with a word are its **connotation.**

The bold words in each pair of sentences below have similar denotations, but their connotations are different. Write the feelings you associate with each word and whether they are positive or negative.

1. The day was **crisp**—just perfect for taking a walk.

_____

2. The day is **raw**. How I wish I'd worn my gloves.

_____

3. Alicia is really **goofy**.

_____

4. Alicia is really **funny**.

_____

5. Juan was **thrifty** and saved his money.

_____

6. Juan was **cheap** and spent hardly any of his money.

_____

TEKS **4.2 (E)** Use a dictionary to determine the meaning of
unknown words.

A. Reading Strategy: Set a Purpose for Reading

As you read, think about your purpose for reading. You might set your own purpose for reading, or your teacher might set a purpose for you. Choose a text that you will read this week, and complete the activity.

Study the chart. Then complete the statements.

Genre	Possible Purposes for Reading
Fiction/Drama/Poetry	to be entertained, to think about a subject in a new way, to understand something about life or people
Informational Text	to learn about a subject, to learn how to do something
Persuasive Text	to learn about a subject, to form an opinion about something, to decide whether to take an action

The genre that I will read is _____.

The subject of the text is _____.

My purpose for reading is to _____.

B. Independent Reading Log

Choose something you would like to read. After reading, complete the reading log. Be sure to paraphrase, or tell the main idea or meaning of the text. Keep the details or events in the correct order. You may use the log to talk to others about what you read.

Genre _____

Title _____

Author _____

This Text Is About _____

_____

_____

TEKS **4.9** Read independently for a sustained period of time and paraphrase what the reading was about, maintaining meaning and logical order. **RC-4 (A)** Establish purposes for reading selected texts based upon own or others' desired outcome to enhance comprehension.

Because of Winn-Dixie **45**
Grade 4/Unit 1

When added to the beginning of a word, a **prefix** changes the meaning of the word.

The prefixes **un-**, **non-**, and **dis-** mean "not" or "the opposite of."

- **dis** + trust = distrust   to not trust
- **non** + sense = nonsense   something that doesn't make sense
- **un** + covered = uncovered   the opposite of covered

The prefix **mis-** means "badly" or "incorrectly."

- **mis** + spell = misspell   to spell incorrectly

Each of these prefixes has a short vowel sound.

Underline the prefix in the following words. Then write the meaning of the word.

1. disobey _____

2. unsure _____

3. misbehave _____

4. nonsense _____

5. unhappy _____

6. dislike _____

7. misunderstand _____

8. disconnect _____

9. unbelievable _____

10. miscalculate _____

© Macmillan/McGraw-Hill

TEKS **4.2 (A)** Determine the meaning of grade-level academic English words derived from Latin, Greek, or other linguistic affixes.

Name _____

injustice ancestors unfair
numerous segregation avoided

Use the clues below to complete the vocabulary word puzzle.

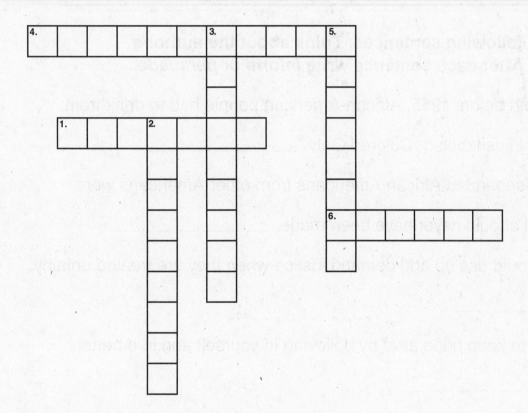

Across

1. kept away from
4. the practice of separating one racial group from another
6. unjust, unreasonable

Down

2. unfairness, an unjust act
3. people from whom one is descended
5. many

TEKS 4.2 (B) Use the context of the sentence to determine the meaning of unfamiliar words.

My Brother Martin
Grade 4/Unit 2
47

Authors write stories and plays to **entertain**. They write articles and books to **inform** or **explain**. When authors write to **persuade**, they give reasons for their point of view, which is what the authors believe and want you to believe, too. What they write is not always backed up by facts.

A. Read the following sentences. Think about the author's purpose. After each sentence write *inform* or *persuade*.

1. In the South before 1955, African-American people had to drink from water fountains labeled "Colored Only." _____

2. Laws that separated African Americans from other Americans were unjust and should never have been made. _____

3. People should rise up and demand justice when they are treated unfairly. _____

4. You need to keep hope alive by believing in yourself and in a better world. _____

5. In 1955, Rosa Parks was arrested for refusing to give up her seat near the front of a bus. _____

B. Write a sentence to persuade readers to support your point of view on a topic you feel strongly about.

_____

_____

_____

TEKS 4.12 Explain how an author uses language to present information to influence what the reader thinks or does.

Name _____

As you read *My Brother Martin*, fill in the Author's Purpose Map.

Clue	Clue	Clue

Author's Purpose

How does the information you wrote in the Author's Purpose Map help you to understand *My Brother Martin*?

TEKS **5.7** Identify the literary language used in biographies, including how authors present major events in a person's life.

As I read, I will pay attention to intonation and expression.

	Coretta Scott King never planned on being a civil rights
10	leader. She thought she would become a teacher or a singer.
21	Instead, she became a leader in the fight for equal rights.
32	Coretta Scott was born in 1927 in a small town in
42	Alabama. She walked three miles to get to school each
52	morning. And she walked three miles back each afternoon.
61	Every day she watched school buses drive white children to
71	their school.
73	In those days **segregation** was the law in the South.
83	African Americans could not go to certain restaurants.
91	They could not drink from certain water fountains. They
100	had to sit in the back of public buses. Black children and
112	white children went to separate schools.
118	Coretta's father Obadiah (oh-buh-DIGH-uh) was the
123	first African American in his county to own his own truck.
134	Some white truckers felt that he was taking away their
144	business. One day the Scotts came home from church to
154	find that their home had burned down. 161

Comprehension Check

1. What is the author's purpose? **Author's Purpose**

2. Why do you think the Scotts' house was burned down? **Cause and Effect**

	Words Read	–	Number of Errors	=	Words Correct Score
First Read		–		=	
Second Read		–		=	

© Macmillan/McGraw-Hill

TEKS 4.1 Read aloud grade-level stories with fluency and comprehension.

When you read persuasive writing, try to determine the **author's point of view**. An author's point of view is what he or she believes. In persuasive writing, authors use **persuasive language** to influence readers to agree with their point of view. Be careful when you read persuasive writing. Authors do not always back up their writing with facts. Also watch for **loaded language**, such as *always, never, best,* and *special.*

Read the passage. Then answer the questions that follow.

Dear Editor,

I am writing about the awful plan to replace Rose Park with a parking lot. This is a terrible idea! We do not need more parking lots in our town. We have only four parks. People who care about children will not agree to this plan. Even though Rose Park is run-down, the park is still a special place where families gather and children play. Readers, write in and help save Rose Park!

1. What is the author's point of view?

_____

_____

2. How does the author use persuasive language to influence the reader?

_____

_____

3. What does the author want the reader to do?

_____

_____

TEKS 4.12 Explain how an author uses language to present information to influence what the reader thinks or does.

My Brother Martin 51
Grade 4/Unit 2

A **survey** can help you collect information from a large group
of people. Begin by considering what you want to learn. Then
write questions for people to answer. The questions should be
about your topic and should be answered with "Yes," "No," or
"Undecided." To understand the results of the survey, tally the
answers to see how most of the people feel about the topic.

Read the following survey and answer the questions.

Survey for Student Council

Question	Yes	No	Undecided
1. Do you think our playground equipment needs to be replaced?	☐	☐	☐
2. Do you think students should help raise money for new equipment?	☐	☐	☐
3. Do you think the school should have a walk-a-thon to raise money?	☐	☐	☐
4. Do you think the school should hold a bake sale to raise money?	☐	☐	☐

1. Why are all of the questions answered with "Yes," "No," or "Undecided"?

   _____

2. What two ways for raising money are given in this survey?

   _____

3. Why do you think these two ways of raising money are given?

   _____

4. What survey topics can you conduct at your school?

   _____

TEKS 4.24 (A) (i) Collect information from student-initiated surveys.

> The prefix **un-** means "not."   **Unfair** means "not fair."
>
> The prefix **re-** means "again."   **Retell** means "tell again."
>
> The suffix **-able** means "capable of."   **Teachable** means
> "capable of being taught."

A. Circle the phrases in the story that would sound better using the prefixes *un-* or *re-*. Then write the new words below.

"It's terribly not fair, Grandmother!" Cordelia exclaimed. "Wilson School is just three blocks away. Why can't I just keep attending my classes there?"

Cordelia's grandmother looked at the bowl of cold, not eaten soup and left Cordelia's question not answered. "Let me warm again that pea soup for you, honey. You'll feel better after you have had your dinner."

"I know you do not like this, Grandmother. Even though you're not saying anything, I know you're terribly not happy with the new laws. So, why can't you admit that scheduling again our classes miles away is not acceptable!"

Marion looked over her glasses at her granddaughter. "No use talking about it around our kitchen table, child. But there will be talk all over this great land of ours. And mark my words, Cordelia; these not fortunate days will not go not noticed."

_____   _____   _____

_____   _____   _____

_____

B. Find the word with the suffix *-able* in the story. Write the word and its meaning on the line provided.

_____

TEKS **4.2 (A)** Determine the meaning of grade-level academic English words derived from Latin, Greek, and other linguistic affixes.

My Brother Martin   **53**
Grade 4/Unit 2

© Macmillan/McGraw-Hill

A. Reading Strategy: Ask Questions

Asking questions can help you understand what you read. Some questions help you think about what a text says. Choose a text that you are reading this week, and complete the activity.

Use the chart to find questions you can ask about the text.

	Fiction/ Drama	Poetry	Biography/ Autobiography	Informational/ Persuasive Text
What does the text say about . . .	a character, an event, or the setting	the subject or the speaker's feelings	the person's thoughts or actions; the events	the topic; causes and effects; the author's views

Fill in the blanks to ask and answer questions about the text.

Question: What does the text say about _____?

Answer: _____

Question: What does the text say about _____?

Answer: _____

B. Independent Reading Log

Choose something you would like to read. After reading, complete the reading log. Be sure to paraphrase, or tell the main idea or meaning of the text. Keep the details or events in the correct order. You may use the log to talk to others about what you read.

Genre _____

Title _____

Author _____

This Text Is About _____

_____

TEKS **4.9** Read independently for a sustained period of time and paraphrase what the reading was about, maintaining meaning and logical order.
RC-4 (B) Ask literal, interpretive, and evaluative questions of text.

Name _____

> The letter pairs **ch**, **sh**, **th**, **wh**, and **ph** have one sound, even though there are two letters in the pair. Say the following words aloud and listen to the one sound made by the letter pairs.
>
> - **th** <u>th</u>irty, bo<u>th</u>er
> - **ph** <u>ph</u>rase, head<u>ph</u>one
> - **ch** <u>ch</u>air, ar<u>ch</u>way
> - **sh** <u>sh</u>ove, wa<u>sh</u>er
> - **wh** <u>wh</u>irl, any<u>wh</u>ere

Use the clues to fill in the blanks with words that have ch, sh, ph, wh, or th.

1. I gave the money to my mother and _____.

2. I made a _____ before I blew out the candles on my birthday cake.

3. _____ is the library? Is it near Flower Street?

4. My camera helps me take good _____.

5. We stopped to rest on the park _____.

6. I'm going to the dentist because I have a cavity in one _____.

7. I picked up the _____ and called my friend.

8. Today I have crackers and _____ for a snack.

9. I put the plates, forks, and knives into the _____ and turned it on.

10. I made a bar _____ to show the daily sales of my lemonade stand.

| muttered | gaped | insult |
| snickering | legendary | flinched |

A. Choose the correct word from the box to complete each sentence.

1. Jorge was angry because Tammy kept _____ when he struck out.

2. Jackie Robinson was a _____ baseball player. He was famous for his many skills.

3. When she missed the throw to first base, Danisha _____ quietly to herself.

4. I was so shocked when we won the baseball game that I

_____ at my teammates in surprise.

5. I _____ when the ball came close to me.

6. Carla told Jefferson that he was a bad player. That was an

_____ .

B. Use three of the above words in sentences of your own.

7. _____

8. _____

9. _____

TEKS **4.2 (B)** Use the context of the sentence to determine the meaning of unfamiliar words.

> Authors write to **entertain**, to **inform**, or to **persuade**.

Read the passages and answer the questions.

Theo sat on the bench and watched as Molly went to bat. She took a big swing at the first pitch and missed. On the next pitch she surprised everyone and bunted the ball. It rolled slowly towards third base, and Molly sprinted to first. She got to first safely. Theo thought to himself, "Wow, that was pretty tricky. The fielders thought that she was going to hit the ball hard, so they weren't ready for that bunt. Maybe I could try that some time."

1. What was the author's purpose in writing this story? _____

2. What helped you decide on the author's purpose?

_____

_____

Jackie Robinson is a member of the Baseball Hall of Fame. Born in 1919 in Cairo, Georgia, Robinson went to college at the University of California in Los Angeles. He played baseball after college and became the first African-American baseball player in the major leagues. He played for the Brooklyn Dodgers for ten years. During that time they won six pennants. Robinson stole home 19 times and was named the Most Valuable Player in 1949.

3. What was the author's purpose in writing the passage? _____

4. What helped you decide on the author's purpose?

_____

_____

TEKS 5.7 Identify the literary language used in biographies, including how authors present major events in a person's life.

As you read *Mighty Jackie*, fill in the Author's Purpose Map.

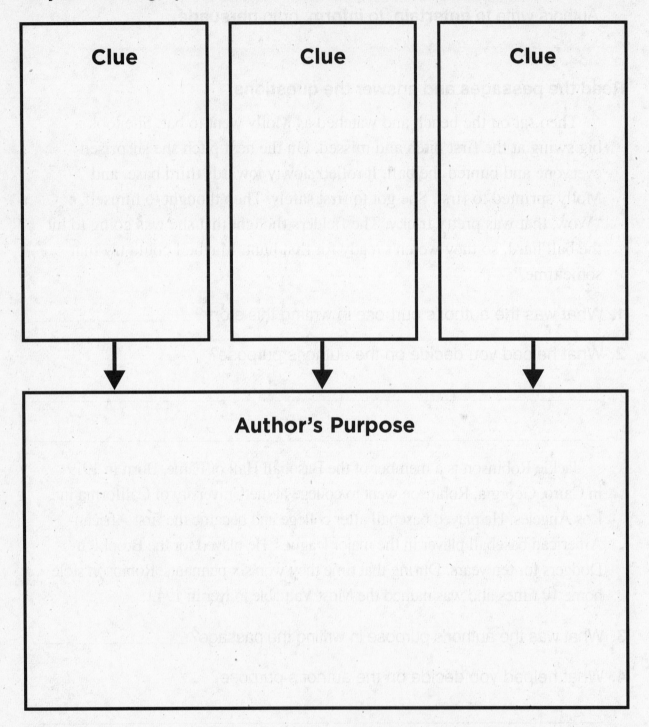

Clue	Clue	Clue

Author's Purpose

How does the information you wrote in the Author's Purpose Map
help you understand *Mighty Jackie*?

TEKS 5.7 Identify the literary language used in biographies, including how
authors present major events in a person's life.

As I read, I will pay attention to intonation and expression.

	Mildred Ella Didrikson was born on June 26, 1914, in
8	Port Arthur, Texas. Mildred's father built a gym for his
18	children in the backyard. The children played many sports,
27	including baseball. Mildred was a good hitter. So the boys
37	started calling her "Babe," after the **legendary** baseball
45	player Babe Ruth. Ruth was famous for hitting home runs.
55	It was no fluke that Babe Didrikson became a good athlete.
66	Babe's father read newspaper articles about the 1928
73	Olympic Games aloud to his children. Babe was 14 years
82	old at the time. She began to dream about competing in the
94	Olympics someday.
96	Babe attended high school during the late 1920s. She
104	excelled in every sport she tried. At only 5 feet (152 cm)
114	tall and 105 pounds (48 kg), Babe was small. But she was
124	strong. 125

Comprehension Check

1. Why does the author make it a point to explain Mildred Didrikson's nickname? **Author's Purpose**

2. How did Babe Didrikson's home life help her to become an athlete? **Plot Development**

	Words Read	–	Number of Errors	=	Words Correct Score
First Read		–		=	
Second Read		–		=	

TEKS 4.1 Read aloud grade-level stories with fluency and comprehension.

Mighty Jackie • **Grade 4/Unit 2** 59

When you **compare** and **contrast** two things, you find ways in which they are alike or different. **Text structure** is the way in which a text is organized. Authors sometimes organize their writing by comparison and contrast. Signal words such as *like, both, also, most, but, whereas,* and *however* may tell you when things are being compared and contrasted. When authors do not use signal words, the relationship between the two things is implicit, or not directly stated. You must infer how the two things compare or contrast.

Read the passage. Then complete the items that follow.

Babe Ruth and Lou Gehrig played together as New York Yankees in the 1920s and 1930s. The two teammates could not have been more different. Ruth played in the outfield. Gehrig played first base. Ruth was outgoing, whereas Gehrig was quiet. Ruth liked attention, but Gehrig was shy.

Despite their differences, both players were known for hitting home runs. Ruth set several records for the number of home runs hit in a season. Gehrig also set a record by hitting four home runs in one game. Both Ruth and Gehrig are members of the Baseball Hall of Fame.

1. List one way in which Babe Ruth and Lou Gehrig were alike and one way in which they were different.

_____

_____

_____

2. What implicit relationship can you infer from this passage?

_____

TEKS 4.11 (C) Describe explicit and implicit relationships among ideas in texts organized by comparison.

Name _____

A **lyric poem** expresses the poet's feelings in a way that sounds like a song. Lyric poems often use rhyming words and rhythm, or meter. The poem's **meter** is the way the author arranges the accented and unaccented syllables. The author of a lyric poem may use stanzas. A **stanza** is a group of lines. **Line breaks** separate each line in a stanza.

Read the poem and answer the questions.

Mary's Canary

Mary had a pretty bird,

    Feathers bright and yellow,

Slender legs—upon my word

    He was a pretty fellow!

The sweetest note he always sung, _____

    Which much delighted Mary. _____

She often, where the cage was hung, _____

    Sat hearing her canary. _____

1. How many stanzas are in the poem? _____

2. How many lines are in the first stanza? _____

3. What words rhyme in the second stanza? _____

4. Read each line in the second stanza. Count the number of syllables in each line. Write the number on the line.

TEKS 4.4 Explain how the structural elements of poetry relate to form.

Name _____

When you come to a word you do not know in a passage, read the entire sentence. Other words in the sentence may give **clues** to the meaning of the unfamiliar word.

A. Circle the clue words in each sentence that help you figure out the meaning of the word in dark type.

1. The crowd was **stupefied** by how amazingly bad the team played.

2. The children were afraid of the **cantankerous** old man because he was angry and always yelled at them.

3. The whole-grain cereal was full of **nutrients** that keep athletes healthy.

4. Aldo hit the ball so hard that no one even saw the ball fly **swiftly** through the air.

5. The new stadium was so **colossal** that you could fit 80,000 people into it and still have tickets left over.

B. Write your own definitions for three of the words above. First write the word. Then write what it means.

6. _____

7. _____

8. _____

TEKS **4.2 (B)** Use the context of the sentence to determine the meaning of unfamiliar words.

A. Reading Strategy: Ask Questions

Asking questions can help you understand what you read. Some questions help you think about what a text says. Choose a text that you are reading this week, and complete the activity.

You can ask different questions for different kinds of texts. Decide which kind of text you are reading. Then write questions for that text.

Nonfiction	Question based on the title: _____ _____? Question based on a picture: _____ _____? Question based on a topic sentence: _____ _____?
Fiction	Who _____? What _____? Why _____? How _____?

As you read, look for answers to your questions.

B. Book Talk

Choose something you would like to read. Afterward, participate in a teacher-led discussion about the selections that you and your classmates read. You should

• answer questions from your teacher and classmates with appropriate detail.

• pose questions about other students' reading with appropriate detail.

• provide suggestions that build upon the ideas of others.

TEKS 4.9 Read independently for a sustained period of time.
RC-4 (B) Ask literal, interpretive, and evaluative questions of text.

Mighty Jackie
Grade 4/Unit 2 **63**

In some **three-letter blends**, you hear the sounds of the three consonants, as in *scrape* and *strain*. Sometimes, a three-letter blend is formed by a digraph and a third consonant, as in *shrug* and *thread*.

A. Circle the three-letter blend at the beginning of each word.

1. s p l e n d i d
2. s h r i n k
3. t h r o n e
4. s t r e a m
5. s p l a s h

6. t h r e a d
7. s h r i m p
8. s c r u n c h
9. s p l i t
10. t h r o u g h

B. Read the paragraph below. Circle six words that begin with a three-letter blend. Then continue the story. Use at least two words that begin with a three-letter blend and circle the words.

It was the first swim meet of the spring season. Juan climbed onto the starting block at the edge of the pool. He shrugged his shoulders to loosen his muscles, then plunged into the water, hardly making a splash. As his strong arms cut through the water, he saw his closest opponent about three feet behind him.

_____

_____

_____

_____

TEKS 3.1 (E) Monitor accuracy in decoding.

Name _____

| similar | challenges | designed |
| achieved | varied | |

A. Write a complete sentence to answer each question below. In your answer, use the vocabulary word in bold type.

1. Why do you think goalball might be **similar** to soccer?

   _____

   _____

2. What is one of the **challenges** that an athlete with physical disabilities

   might face? _____

   _____

3. What kind of equipment might be specially **designed** for an athlete in the

   Paralympics? _____

   _____

4. What are two of the **varied** games included in the Paralympics?

   _____

   _____

5. What is something that you **achieved** in the past last year?

   _____

   _____

B. Now use one of the words above in a sentence of your own.

6. _____

   _____

TEKS **4.2 (B)** Use the context of the sentence to determine the meaning of unfamiliar words.

Making a Splash
Grade 4/Unit 2   65

> The **main idea** is what a paragraph is mostly about. A main idea can be **explicit**, or stated at the beginning of the paragraph. A main idea can also be **implied**, meaning that readers must think about how the details in the text are related.

Read the passage. Then answer the questions below.

Beep Baseball is a lot like baseball. It uses a ball. It uses bases. It has two teams. The players use a bat to hit the ball.

Unlike players on baseball teams, the players on Beep Baseball teams are sighted and non-sighted people. The sport is played with a big ball and a big bat. There are only two bases, which look like soft towers.

When a batter hits a ball, one of the bases begins to beep loudly. The batter runs toward the sound. If the batter can reach the base before someone throws a ball to the base, his or her team scores a point.

1. What is the main idea of the first paragraph?

_____

2. Is that main idea explicit or implied?

_____

3. What is a detail that supports that main idea?

_____

4. The main idea of the second paragraph is implied, or not stated. What is the main idea of this paragraph?

_____

5. Is the main idea of the third paragraph explicit or implied?

_____

6. What would be a good main idea sentence for the third paragraph?

_____

TEKS 4.11 (A) Summarize the main idea and supporting details in text in ways that maintain meaning.

Name _____

As you read "Leg Work," fill in the Main Idea and Details Chart.

Detail
Detail
Detail
Main Idea

How does the information you wrote in the Main Idea and Details Chart help you understand the information presented in "Leg Work"?

TEKS **4.11 (A)** Summarize the main idea and supporting details in text in ways that maintain meaning.

Making a Splash
Grade 4/Unit 2

67

Name _____

As I read, I will focus on reading accurately.

	"Are we there yet?" Jamal asked, crossing his arms
9	across his chest.
12	"Almost, honey," his mom replied. "Look out the
20	window. Isn't it beautiful?"
24	Jamal didn't answer, but he did look. Out his mom's
34	window, all he could see was a rising, rocky cliff. Out his
46	own window, the cliff dropped down, and Jamal could see
56	the road winding below them. Below that were green
65	fields. A few houses and farms were scattered about.
74	The city was a long way away. It felt like they had been
87	driving forever.
89	They were driving up into the mountains to spend a
99	week at a ranch. His mom had lived at this ranch when
111	she was a little girl. "Some vacation," Jamal thought to
121	himself. 122

Comprehension Check

1. How does Jamal feel about his vacation? **Plot Development**

2. How does Jamal's mom feel about the vacation? **Plot Development**

	Words Read	–	Number of Errors	=	Words Correct Score
First Read		–		=	
Second Read		–		=	

TEKS 4.1 Read aloud grade-level stories with fluency and comprehension.

Name _____

Sometimes authors directly **state** their purpose for writing, but usually the **author's purpose** is **implied**. When the purpose is implied, readers must make inferences to determine whether the purpose is to entertain, inform, persuade, or explain.

Read *Making a Splash*, and fill in the Author's Purpose Map.

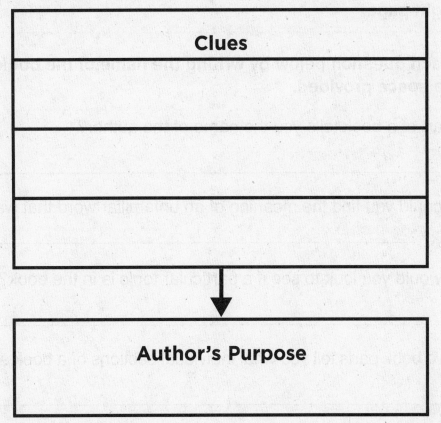

Clues

Author's Purpose

Is the author's purpose in *Making a Splash* stated or implied? Explain how you know.

_____

_____

_____

_____

TEKS **4.10** Explain the difference between a stated and an implied purpose for an expository text.

Looking at the different parts of a book can help you figure out if the book will have the information you need. If you use a book as a source for a report, remember to note the author, title, publisher, and publication year.

title page	**table of contents**	**index**
glossary	**headings**	**subheadings**
copyright page		

Answer each question below by writing the name of the book part in the space provided.

1. What part of a book tells you the name of the author?

   _____

2. Where could you find the meaning of an unfamiliar word that was used in the book? _____

3. Where would you look to see if a particular topic is in the book?

   _____

4. What two book parts tell you what individual sections of a book are about?

   _____

5. What part of the book tells you the names of chapters in the book?

   _____

6. Choose a book and identify the author, title, publisher, and year of publication.

   _____

TEKS 4.24 (D) Identify the author, title, publisher, and publication year of sources.

Name _____

To understand the meaning of an **idiom**, you need to use the words and phrases around the idiom or think about how you might have heard the expression before.

A. Read the idioms in the box. Find and underline the idioms in the sentences below. Then circle the words in the sentence that help you understand the expression.

has a green thumb	get the hang of it
make a splash	lend a hand

1. I'd be happy to lend a hand and help you paint your room.

2. When you see all her healthy plants, it's easy to figure out that Mrs. Potts has a green thumb.

3. It took me a long time to learn how to download pictures onto my computer, but now that I get the hang of it, I do it all the time.

4. Unlike my friend who always likes to make a vivid impression on people, I don't usually like to make a splash.

B. Read the idioms below. Think about how you have heard them used. Then write a sentence that includes context clues that would help a reader understand each idiom.

5. catching a cold _____

_____

6. pull my leg _____

_____

Name _____

A. Reading Strategy: Ask Questions

Asking questions can help you understand what you read. Some questions help you think about what a text means. Choose a text that you are reading this week, and complete the activity.

Use the chart to find questions you can ask about the text.

	Fiction/ Drama	Poetry	Biography/ Autobiography	Informational/ Persuasive Text
What is the meaning of . . .	a character's actions; an event that takes place	the way that the poem's subject is described	the subject's words or actions; events that take place	details that the author includes

Fill in the blanks to ask and answer questions about the text.

Question: What is the meaning of _____?

Answer: _____

Question: What is the meaning of _____?

Answer: _____

B. Independent Reading Log

Choose something you would like to read. After reading, complete the reading log. Be sure to paraphrase, or tell the main idea or meaning of the text. Keep the details or events in the correct order. You may use the log to talk to others about what you read.

Genre _____

Title _____

Author _____

This Text Is About _____

_____

TEKS **4.9** Read independently for a sustained period of time and paraphrase what the reading was about, maintaining meaning and logical order.
RC-4 (B) Ask literal, interpretive, and evaluative questions of text.

Name _____

Sometimes when the letter **r** comes after a vowel, the sound of the short vowel changes. Say the following words aloud and notice the sound of the vowels.

bat   bar   cat   cart   fox   floor

The sounds of these vowels are shown as **/är/** and **/ôr/**.

Circle the word with /är/ or /ôr/ to complete each sentence. Then write /är/ or /ôr/ on the blank at the end.

1. Please close the _____ when you leave. _____

    dear   door   dare

2. The _____ used watercolors to finish his painting. _____

    roar   rear   artist

3. The _____ on the rosebush are sharp. _____

    horns   thorns   stars

4. Ben Franklin's inventions _____ still in use today. _____

    care   core   are

5. We are going to have a birthday _____. _____

    party   pat   trap

6. My new _____ is nice and warm. _____

    scarf   calm   pretty

descendants	habitat	threatened
emerge	fragile	sanctuary

Label each statement *True* or *False*. If the statement is false, explain why.

1. Something is *fragile* if it is hard to break.

_____

2. The desert is the whale's natural *habitat*.

_____

3. When the Sun does not *emerge* from behind the clouds, the day is very bright and sunny.

_____

4. Children are *descendants* of their grandparents.

_____

5. If you think you are safe from harm, you may feel *threatened*.

_____

6. A *sanctuary* is a place where wild animals can live safely.

_____

7. Write a sentence that contains two of the above vocabulary words.

_____

TEKS 4.2 (B) Use the context of the sentence to determine the meaning of unfamiliar words.

Name _____

> A **cause** makes something else happen. When you ask the
> question "Why did that happen?" the answer is the cause.
> What happens as a result of the cause is its **effect**. When you
> ask the question "What happened?" the answer is the effect.

Read the passage below. Then answer the questions that follow.

Every spring my family goes on a camping trip. My parents like to get out of the city, and they want my brother and me to enjoy nature. When we first leave the city, I'm always surprised by the quiet. There are no more sirens or blaring horns, because there is no traffic.

Since we love to "rough it," we bring only what we really need. We have sleeping bags, cooking equipment, and food. We set up camp near a mountain river. Because the river water comes from melting snow, we keep food that can spoil in a container in the water. We put a big rock on top so our food doesn't float away.

Our week in the mountains is fun for the entire family. It brings us together, and, for a little while, we forget about our hectic city lives. We all look forward to our yearly camping trip when we all slow down and enjoy the peace and beauty of nature.

1. What causes the family to go on a camping trip every spring?

_____

2. What is the effect of driving where there is no traffic?

_____

3. What causes the river's cold temperature? _____

4. What effect does the yearly camping trip have on the family?

_____

TEKS **4.11 (C)** Describe explicit and implicit relationships among ideas in texts organized by cause-and-effect.

As you read *Wild Horses,* fill in the Cause and Effect Chart.

Cause	→	Effect
	→	
	→	
	→	
	→	

How does the information you wrote in the Cause and Effect Chart
help you understand how the author organized ideas in *Wild Horses*?

TEKS **4.11 (C)** Describe explicit and implicit relationships among ideas in
texts organized by cause-and-effect.

Name _____

As I read, I will pay attention to my reading rate.

	By the 1800s, huge herds of wild horses were roaming the
10	open range.
12	Picture this: You must catch a wild animal that can run as
24	fast as a train. You must tame that wild animal by riding on its
38	back. You must teach that animal to follow your every command.
49	And you must trust that animal with your life.
58	That is exactly what cowboys did when they caught, tamed,
68	and rode wild mustangs.
72	Capturing a wild mustang was a team effort. One cowboy
82	could not do it alone. Cowboys rode together on tamed horses in
94	order to catch the wild mustangs. The cowboys used their fastest
105	and strongest horses to chase the wild mustangs.
113	When the wild mustangs were exhausted, the cowboys drove
122	them into a fenced corral. The mustangs couldn't see the fence
133	until it was too late. Tired and thirsty from the long chase and
146	glistening with sweat, the mustangs could run no more. 155

Comprehension Check

1. What was the effect that a cowboy obtained by following these steps?
Cause and Effect

2. How were mustangs captured? **Main Idea and Details**

	Words Read	–	Number of Errors	=	Words Correct Score
First Read		–		=	
Second Read		–		=	

© Macmillan/McGraw-Hill

TEKS 4.1 Read aloud grade-level stories with fluency and comprehension.

When you read **independently**, you read on your own. Before you read, first set a purpose, or reason, for reading. For example, you may read for enjoyment, to follow steps in a procedure, or to learn more about a topic. After you read, **paraphrase** the text. When paraphrasing, put the main ideas and important details into your own words without changing the meaning of the text.

A. Read the title of the passage. Then answer the question below.

1. What purpose could you set for reading the passage?

_____

_____

B. Now read the passage independently. Then paraphrase the passage on the lines below.

Audie Murphy: American War Hero

On June 20 every year, Texans hold Audie Murphy Day. Audie Murphy was born in Texas in 1924. He was an American war hero during World War II. He was wounded three times during the war. After the war, he was the most honored American soldier. For his brave acts in battle, Murphy received every honor the United States gave soldiers for bravery. He also received awards from other countries. When Murphy came home from the war, he became a writer. He wrote about his time in the war. He also became an actor. He appeared in 45 movies. On Audie Murphy Day, people remember his life and his brave acts. In Farmersville, there is a parade in his honor.

_____

_____

_____

_____

_____

© Macmillan/McGraw-Hill

TEKS **4.9** Read independently for a sustained period of time and paraphrase what the reading was about, maintaining meaning and logical order.

A **metaphor** is a comparison of two things that are not alike without the use of *like* or *as*.

Hyperbole is the use of exaggeration for emphasis or to make a point.

Read the following sentences. Put a check in the box for the sentences that contain hyperbole. Underline the hyperbole. Put an X in the box for the sentences that contain metaphors. Circle the two things that are being compared.

1. Suzie is so fast she can run two miles before you've put on your shoes. ☐

2. Timothy is a snail when it comes to making his bed. ☐

3. Jim used a lasso to catch a hundred horses at once. ☐

4. This pillow is a cloud. I love sleeping on it. ☐

5. The emerald eyes of the cat shone in the darkness. ☐

6. My baby sister is an angel. I can't wait to see her. ☐

7. She was so thirsty she drank a lake and said she was still thirsty! ☐

TEKS 4.8 Identify the author's use of metaphors to produce imagery.

Wild Horses **79**
Grade 4/Unit 2

> **Context clues** can help readers determine the meaning of unfamiliar words. Sometimes, the other words and sentences in the paragraph can help you figure out the word's meaning.

A. Read the passage below. Use context clues to help you figure out the meanings of the words in dark type.

We were standing around the **corral**, leaning on the fence and watching the horses. "Midnight's a good mother," I said, as the black mare's **foal** followed closely behind her. Only two days old, it was still getting used to walking on its long, **wobbly** legs.

My aunt sighed. "Sometimes I wonder if they would have been better off in the canyon, living in the **wilderness** instead of around people," she said.

B. Write the definition for each word, along with the context clues that helped you identify the word's meaning.

1. corral   definition: _____

context clues: _____

2. foal   definition: _____

context clues: _____

3. wobbly   definition: _____

context clues: _____

4. wilderness   definition: _____

context clues: _____

TEKS **4.2 (B)** Use the context of the sentence to determine the meaning of unfamiliar words.

Name _____

A. Reading Strategy: Ask Questions

Asking questions can help you understand what you read. Some questions help you think about what a text means. Choose a text that you are reading this week, and complete the chart.

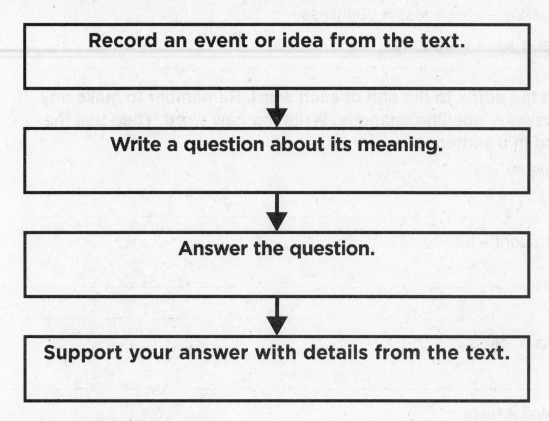

Record an event or idea from the text.

↓

Write a question about its meaning.

↓

Answer the question.

↓

Support your answer with details from the text.

B. Independent Reading Log

Choose something you would like to read. After reading, complete the reading log. Be sure to paraphrase, or tell the main idea or meaning of the text. Keep the details or events in the correct order. You may use the log to talk to others about what you read.

Genre _____

Title _____

Author _____

This Text Is About _____

_____

_____

© Macmillan/McGraw-Hill

TEKS 4.9 Read independently for a sustained period of time and paraphrase what the reading was about, maintaining meaning and logical order.
RC-4 (B) Ask literal, interpretive, and evaluative questions of text.

Wild Horses 81
Grade 4/Unit 2

The suffixes **-y, -ly, -ful, -less**, and **-ness** can be added to the end of a root or base word to change its meaning. Sometimes spelling changes are necessary:

penny – y + i + less = penniless

sun + n + y = sunny

Add the suffix to the end of each word. Remember to make any necessary spelling changes. Write the new word. Then use the word in a sentence.

1. happy + ly = _____

_____

2. thought + ful = _____

_____

_____

3. care + less = _____

_____

4. kind + ness = _____

_____

_____

5. fun + y = _____

_____

6. cheer + ful + ly = _____

_____

7. grace + ful + ness = _____

_____

8. hope + less + ly = _____

_____

© Macmillan/McGraw-Hill

TEKS **4.2 (A)** Determine the meaning of grade-level academic English words derived from Latin, Greek, and other linguistic affixes.

| mysterious | responsibility | midst |
| loosened | amazement | sores |

A. Choose the correct vocabulary word from the list to complete the sentence. Write the words on the lines.

David had a dog. He knew it was his **1.** _____ to take care of Spot. Of course, they had fun together. They played and ran and

explored. Then one day, in the **2.** _____ of having fun, Spot ran through some poison ivy. He soon was covered with painful

3. _____. David took his dog home and washed Spot as best he could. He wrapped Spot up in a quilt and sat with him on the porch. At first, Spot tried to scratch. Then a

4. _____ thing began to happen. Spot stopped wriggling and trying to scratch. David **5.** _____ the quilt and looked

at Spot's legs in **6.** _____. They were still red and swollen. Somehow, having his owner take care of him had calmed him down.

B. Add two sentences to the passage.

7. _____

_____

_____

8. _____

TEKS **4.2 (B)** Use the context of the sentence to determine the meaning of unfamiliar words.

Recognizing the **sequence**, or order, in which things happen in a story helps you better understand what you read.

A. Read the passage below. Then number the sentences below to show the sequence of events.

The Plains Indians lived in North America before the Europeans came. Since they had no horses, the Plains Indians traveled on foot. To hunt buffalo, they would surround a herd and shoot the buffalo with bows and arrows.

This changed when Spanish explorers came to North America and brought horses with them. Now the Plains Indians hunters were able to ride horses and follow buffalo over long distances. They carried tipis with them and set up camps. The hunters could kill buffalo and pull them back to camp using their horses.

Later, guns again changed the way that Plains Indians hunted.

1. _____ Spanish explorers brought horses to North America.

2. _____ The Plains Indians used horses and traveled long distances to hunt buffalo.

3. _____ The Plains Indians hunted buffalo on foot before the Europeans came to North America.

4. _____ The Plains Indians used guns to hunt buffalo.

B. Add an event to the paragraphs and tell where it belongs in the sequence of events.

_____

_____

© Macmillan/McGraw-Hill

TEKS 4.11 (C) Describe implicit relationships among ideas in texts organized by sequence.

Name _____

As you read *Mystic Horse*, fill in the Sequence Chart.

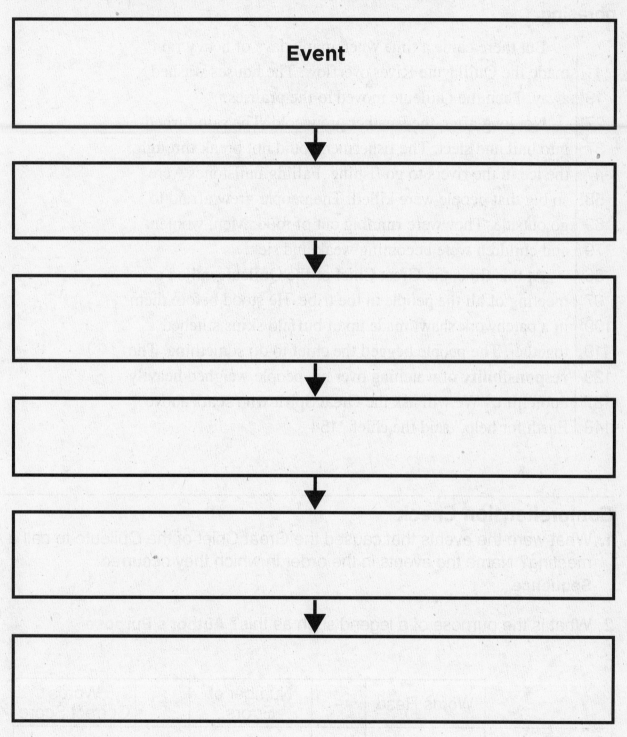

Event

How does the Sequence Chart help you to summarize the plot of
Mystic Horse?

Name _____

As I read, I will pay attention to my expression and phrasing.

	But there came a time when many days of heavy rain
11	made the Quillayute River overflow. The houses washed
19	away. Then the Quileute moved to the prairies.
27	Not long after, the weather grew cold. The rain turned
37	into hail and sleet. The fishermen could not break through
47	the ice in the rivers to go fishing. Falling hailstones were
58	so big that people were killed. The people grew afraid to
69	go outside. They were running out of food. Men, women,
79	and children were becoming weak and sick.
86	At this time, the Great Chief of the Quileute called a
97	meeting of all the people in the tribe. He stood before them
109	in a patchwork shawl made up of buffalo skins stitched
119	together. The people begged the chief to do something. The
129	**responsibility** of watching over his people weighed heavily
137	upon him. "We will ask the Great Spirit who soars above
148	Earth for help," said the chief. 154

Comprehension Check

1. What were the events that caused the Great Chief of the Quileute to call a meeting? Name the events in the order in which they occurred.
   Sequence

2. What is the purpose of a legend such as this? **Author's Purpose**

	Words Read	–	Number of Errors	=	Words Correct Score
First Read		–		=	
Second Read		–		=	

© Macmillan/McGraw-Hill

TEKS 4.1 Read aloud grade-level stories with fluency and comprehension.

86 Mystic Horse • **Grade 4/Unit 2**

A **fable** is a short story that usually has animal characters. These animal **characters** often have human traits and feelings. Fables end with a **moral**, or lesson, that readers can apply to their own experiences.

Read each fable and complete the items below.

1. An ant passed a butterfly in a cocoon, about to finish its change. The butterfly moved its tail, catching the ant's attention. The ant saw the butterfly all wrapped up in its cocoon. The ant boasted, "Look at you, stuck there. You are not able to move while I can run and play." The butterfly did not reply. A few days later, the ant passed the spot again. The butterfly was gone. Only the cocoon remained. The ant wondered what happened to the creature inside when above him, a beautiful butterfly spread his wings.

    "Boast now that you can run and play," said the butterfly. He flapped his wings and flew high into the sky.

2. One day, a hare passed a tortoise plodding along on her way. The hare made fun of the tortoise's short legs and slow pace.

    "I am twice as fast as you," the hare boasted. The tortoise said, "I may have short legs. I may not be as fast as you. Yet, I bet that I can beat you in a race."

    The hare laughed at such a silly idea. He quickly agreed to the race. During the race, the hare knew that he would win. He was sleepy, so he decided to rest on the side of the road. The hare fell asleep. When he woke up, he hurried to finish the race. The tortoise had already crossed the finish line. "Slow and steady wins the race," the tortoise said.

• How do the hare and the ant compare? How do they contrast?

_____

_____

_____

© Macmillan/McGraw-Hill

TEKS **4.3 (B)** Compare and contrast the adventures or exploits of characters in traditional and classical literature.

Name _____

> A **chart** presents factual information—such as names, places, and numbers—in a compact form.

Look at the chart from a sports almanac. Then use the chart to answer the questions that follow.

The Top Five Pitchers in Baseball History

Name	Career Length	Games Won	Games Lost
Walter Johnson	21 years	417	279
Christy Matthewson	17 years	373	188
Sandy Koufax	12 years	165	87
Lefty Grove	17 years	300	141
Cy Young	22 years	511	316

1. What does this chart tell you about these pitchers? _____

   _____

2. Which of the pitchers had the shortest career? _____

3. Which pitcher won the most games? _____

4. Which pitcher lost the fewest number of games? _____

5. Which pitchers had careers that lasted the same number of years?

   _____

6. Who has the highest numbers in all three categories? _____

TEKS 4.13 (B) Explain factual information presented graphically.

Name _____

Homophones are pairs of words that are pronounced the same but have different spellings and meanings. You can use a dictionary to check the meanings of homophones.

here / hear	needed / kneaded	plains / planes
there / their	seen / scene	buries / berries
rain / rein	four / for	road / rode
blue / blew	through / threw	

Read the passage. Write *correct* on the lines below if the right homophone is used. If the wrong homophone is used, write the correct word on the line. Use a dictionary to check the meanings of unfamiliar words.

Some Native Americans lived on the <u>planes</u> in the middle of our country.
1

The land <u>their</u> is beautiful. The sky is <u>blue</u>, and tall grass seems to go on
2   3

forever. Even today, the miles of grass are a beautiful <u>scene</u>. The Native
4

Americans <u>road</u> their horses <u>threw</u> the <u>plains</u> hunting buffalo <u>four</u> food.
5   6   7   8

They also ate <u>berries</u> and nuts to add to <u>there</u> diet. It was a hard life but the
9   10

Native Americans were proud of the life they lived.

1. _____   6. _____

2. _____   7. _____

3. _____   8. _____

4. _____   9. _____

5. _____   10. _____

TEKS 4.2 (E) Use a dictionary to determine the meanings of unknown words.

Mystic Horse • Grade 4/Unit 2   **89**

A. Reading Strategy: Ask Questions

Asking questions can help you understand what you read. Some questions help you think about how well a text is written. Choose a text that you are reading this week, and complete the activity.

1. Ask and answer questions about the purpose of the text.

Why was the text written? _____

_____

What events or ideas in the text help it meet that purpose?

_____

_____

2. Ask and answer questions about the author's message.

What is the author's message? _____

_____

What events or ideas in the text help the author express that message?

_____

_____

B. Independent Reading Log

Choose something you would like to read. After reading, complete the reading log. Be sure to paraphrase, or tell the main idea or meaning of the text. Keep the details or events in the correct order. You may use the log to talk to others about what you read.

Genre _____

Title _____

Author _____

This Text Is About _____

_____

_____

TEKS **4.9** Read independently for a sustained period of time and paraphrase what the reading was about, maintaining meaning and logical order. **RC-4 (B)** Ask literal, interpretive, and evaluative questions of text.

Name _____

The **/ûr/** sound can be spelled **er, ir,** and **ur.** The sound is found in words such as **serpent, bird,** and **turkey.**

A. Underline the *vowel + r combination* that represents the /ûr/ sound in each of these words.

1. b u r d e n   2. w h i r l w i n d

3. s t e r n l y   4. b u r r o w

5. s e r p e n t   6. p u r p o s e

7. b i r t h   8. p e r s o n

9. t u r n i p   10. g i r l f r i e n d

B. Now read the paragraph below. Find and circle six words that have the /ûr/ sound. Then continue the story. Circle the words with the /ûr/ sound.

One day, a raccoon climbed in the window of a house. He found a skirt on the floor. Holding it carefully in his mouth, he took it outside. Then he returned and carried away a small purse. Finally, he emerged with a purple shirt.

_____

_____

_____

_____

© Macmillan/McGraw-Hill

| apologize | genuine | harmless |
| slithered | ambulance | weekdays |

A. Use the correct vocabulary word from the box to fill in the blank.

1. On our hike a snake _____ across the trail.

2. The reptile exhibit at the zoo is open _____ from 10 A.M. to 5 P.M.

3. My encyclopedia says that the green snake we saw in my garden is

_____.

4. An _____ rushed the snakebite victim to the hospital.

5. Evan should _____ for leaving a rubber snake on his sister's pillow.

6. Danielle's snake is _____, not rubber!

B. Write two sentences using one of the vocabulary words.

7. _____

_____

8. _____

_____

© Macmillan/McGraw-Hill

TEKS **4.2 (B)** Use the context of the sentence to determine the meaning of unfamiliar words.

Sometimes you have to use story clues to help you **make inferences** about characters in a story. Look closely at characters' interactions for clues to their relationships.

Read the story. Then make inferences to answer the questions.

Evangeline didn't look up from her book when the new student said hello. She'd already read *Adventures with Reptiles* twice, but she just couldn't put it down. At the end of a chapter, she finally looked up.

"I have that book," Jae said. "It's great. Do you want to come over after school to meet my pet lizard?"

"You bet!"

1. How does Evangeline feel when Jae says hello? How do you know?

_____

_____

2. Is the book Evangeline is reading one of her favorites? Why or why not?

_____

_____

3. What kinds of books would the new student like to read? How do you

know? _____

_____

4. Will Evangeline and the new student become friends? Why or why not?

_____

_____

TEKS **4.6 (B)** Describe the interaction of characters including their
relationships and the changes they undergo.

When I Went to the Library
Grade 4/Unit 3   **93**

Name _____

As you read *When I Went to the Library*, fill in the Inferences Web.

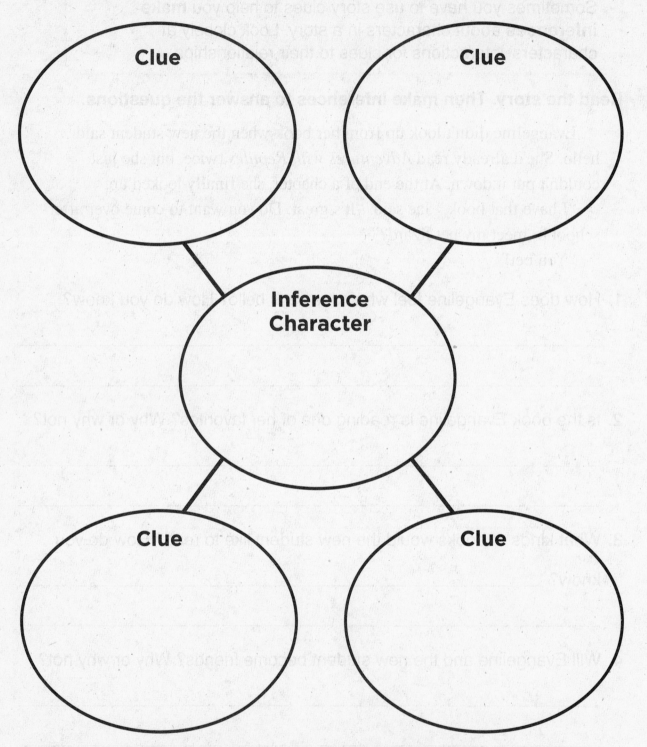

How does the information you wrote in the Inferences Web help you to generate questions about *When I Went to the Library*?

TEKS 4.6 (B) Describe the interaction of characters including their relationships and the changes they undergo.

As I read, I will pay attention to rate and intonation.

	North America is a large area of land. It contains
10	many different climates and landscapes. Most of Mexico
18	and the southwestern United States is hot and dry. Other
28	areas, including the northeastern states and parts of Canada,
37	are cool and wet. Some areas have large mountain ranges,
47	like the Rocky Mountains in the West. Others have flat,
57	rolling plains, like the Midwest.
62	Snakes can be found in just about all of these places.
73	Snakes live in forests, canyons, and deserts. One might
82	even be living in your own backyard. Most snakes don't do
93	well in the cold. In fact, the hardy garter snake is the only
106	serpent that can survive in Alaska.
112	North America has five snake families. Two of these
121	families are poisonous, and three are not. Meet the five
131	families. As you read this book, you will get to know them
143	a lot better. 146

Comprehension Check

1. What is the main idea about snakes in this passage? **Main Idea and Details**

2. Why is there only one kind of snake in Alaska? **Cause and Effect**

	Words Read	−	Number of Errors	=	Words Correct Score
First Read		−		=	
Second Read		−		=	

© Macmillan/McGraw-Hill

TEKS 4.1 Read aloud grade-level stories with fluency and comprehension.

When I Went to the Library
Grade 4/Unit 3   **95**

> **Fiction** stories are made up. They are not about real people
> or events. However, many authors get ideas for stories from
> their own lives. An **autobiography** is a true story written by the
> author about his or her life. Read the following autobiography
> by author Ken Roberts. He explains how he got ideas for the
> fictional story "When I Went to the Library."

Read the passage. Then answer the questions that follow.

The story is based on a real incident. A children's librarian at the
Vancouver Public Library faced this identical situation when two children
came into a branch library with a cardboard box and wanted her to help
identify the snake inside. The librarian did not faint or gasp. She calmly
took the box and the kids over to a wall of reference books and easily
answered their question. She told me and several other librarians this story,
laughing. The second element—fear of snakes—comes from my mother.
My mother is enormously afraid of snakes. Her fear of snakes is legendary
in the family. When I was young we made one of those stick, twisted
rubber band and envelope gadgets that can make a noise like a rattlesnake
and we tricked her into opening the envelope. It was the first and the last
time we ever made fun of her fear.

When I wrote "Dear Mr. Winston" I merely imagined what might have
happened if my mother had been that librarian. It was an easy story to write.

1. How is the fictional character Mr. Winston similar to the author's mother?

_____

2. How are the experiences of the librarian in the above passage and the

librarian in the story different? _____

_____

_____

TEKS **4.7** Identify similarities and differences between the events and
characters' experiences in a fictional work and the actual events and
experiences described in an author's biography or autobiography.

An encyclopedia is a set of books with information on a wide variety of topics. An electronic encyclopedia has the same information, but it is on a CD-ROM. You can use the **toolbar** and **guide words** to find the information you want and gain an overview of the contents of the text.

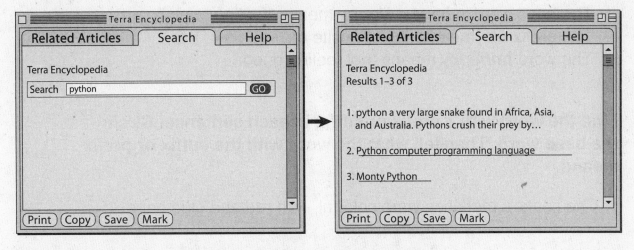

Study the pages above to answer these questions.

1. What information is the computer user looking for? _____

_____

2. Which button on the toolbar should the user click on to print out a copy of

the page? _____

3. If you are looking for a good map of Australia, what button on the toolbar

would you click? _____

4. If you are looking for more information about snakes, what button would

you click? _____

TEKS 4.11 (D) Use multiple text features to gain an overview of the contents of text and to locate information.

When I Went to the Library
Grade 4/Unit 3

97

Name _____

Prefixes and **suffixes** can be added to many words. The original word is called the **base word**. If you know what the base word is, you can figure out the meaning of the word with a prefix or suffix. You can find the meaning of prefixes and suffixes in a dictionary. Many prefixes and suffixes come from Latin, Greek, or other languages.

unhappy
The base word is **happy**. **Happy** means "feeling good."
The prefix **un-** means "the opposite of."
The word **unhappy** means "not feeling good."

Find the word with a prefix or suffix in each sentence. Circle the base word. Then tell what the word with the suffix or prefix means.

1. The snake's markings were colorful, with red and blue bands.

_____

2. Even small snakes can be dangerous sometimes.

_____

3. Knowing that the snake was hidden somewhere in the room made us all uncomfortable.

_____

4. The water moccasin swam under Khalid's boat and disappeared.

_____

5. Casey was successful in finding a picture of a rattlesnake in the book.

_____

© Macmillan/McGraw-Hill

TEKS 4.2 (A) Determine the meaning of grade-level academic English words derived from Latin, Greek, or other linguistic roots and affixes.

Name _____

A. Reading Strategy: Monitor and Adjust Comprehension

Make sure that you understand what you are reading. Comparing
what you are reading and what you already know will help you.
Choose a text that you are reading this week. On a separate sheet of
paper, complete the chart for a difficult part of that text.

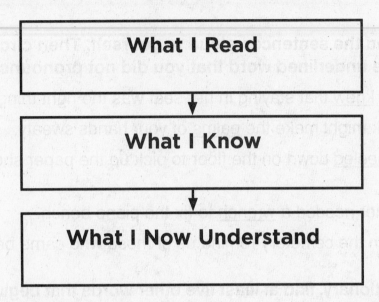

What I Read

What I Know

What I Now Understand

B. Independent Reading Log

Choose something you would like to read. After reading, complete the
reading log. Be sure to paraphrase, or tell the main idea or meaning of
the text. Keep the details or events in the correct order. You may use
the log to talk to others about what you read.

Genre_____

Title _____

Author_____

This Text Is About _____

_____

TEKS **4.9** Read independently for a sustained period of time and paraphrase
what the reading was about, maintaining meaning and logical order.
RC-4 (C) Monitor and adjust comprehension.

When I Went to the Library **99**
Grade 4/Unit 3

Name _____

Say the words below aloud. In each word, the letter in dark type is silent.

knives   plum**b**er   ca**l**m   **w**riggle

A. Quietly read the sentences aloud to yourself. Then circle the letter in the underlined word that you did not pronounce.

1. Rosa Parks <u>knew</u> that staying in her seat was the right thing to do.

2. Taking a risk might make the <u>palms</u> of your hands sweaty.

3. Christine <u>kneeled</u> down on the floor to pick up the paper she had dropped.

4. Martin's father needed a <u>wrench</u> to fix the piano bench.

5. The <u>tombs</u> in the cemetery remind us of those who came before us.

B. Using a dictionary, find at least five other words that begin with *kn* and *wr*. Write these words on the lines below and circle the silent letter in each one.

kn- words	*wr-* words
_____	_____
_____	_____
_____	_____
_____	_____
_____	_____

TEKS 3.1 (E) Monitor accuracy in decoding.
4.22 (A) (v) Spell words with more advanced orthographic patterns and rules: silent letters.

Name _____

A. Use the words in the box to complete the sentences below.

neglected	desperate	obedience
appreciated	endured	misunderstood

1. I play with my dog a lot so she does not feel _____.

2. The only time I scold Sparky is when he tries to eat food from our

   table. Each time he looks at me as if he has _____ great
   suffering.

3. Once I sent him to _____ school.

4. Jill _____ the toys we gave to her dog, especially the ball.

B. Write two sentences, each using one of the vocabulary words.

5. _____

   _____

6. _____

   _____

TEKS 4.2 (B) Use the context of the sentence to determine the meaning of
unfamiliar words.

Name _____

Sometimes authors don't explain how one plot event influences another, so you must **draw conclusions**. When you draw conclusions, you use information from the selection and your own prior experience connected to the reading selection.

Read the story. Answer the questions and draw conclusions.

Fred and Roberto lived next door to each other. Whenever Roberto looked out the window and saw that Fred's owner was taking him for a walk, Roberto would scratch at the front door and whine until Mrs. Marsh got his leash and took him out.

One day, Fred came bounding into Roberto's backyard. "I'm running away," he told Roberto. "Mr. Gomez doesn't appreciate the way I bring him his slippers when he comes home from work."

"Don't do it," Roberto advised Fred. "Give Mr. Gomez a little more time to get to know you. He will appreciate you when he gets to know you better."

"You may be right," Fred agreed. "I'll give him another chance."

1. Why did Roberto scratch on the door?

_____

2. What happened after Roberto scratches on the door?

_____

3. Why did Fred want to run away?

_____

4. Why does Fred agree with Roberto?

_____

TEKS **4.6 (A)** Sequence and summarize the plot's main events and explain their influence on future events.

As you read *Dear Mrs. LaRue*, fill in the Conclusions Chart.

Text Clues	Conclusion

How does completing the Conclusions Chart help you to generate questions about *Dear Mrs. LaRue*?

TEKS 4.6 (A) Sequence and summarize the plot's main events and explain their influence on future events.

Dear Mrs. LaRue • **Grade 4/Unit 3** 103

© Macmillan/McGraw-Hill

As I read, I will pay attention to expression.

	Presidents have kept a wide range of pets. These
9	animals have included cows, mice, goats, and birds. But
18	dogs have been the most popular presidential pets.
26	Dogs are loyal and loving. They make their owners
35	feel appreciated. Like other dog owners, many Presidents
43	have enjoyed the special friendship that dogs can give.
52	Many people believe that dogs help Presidents gain
60	support from Americans. Pictures of Presidents playing
67	with their dogs can make the Presidents seem likable and
77	help them win votes.
81	More than 200 dogs of various breeds have lived at the
91	White House. Some of these White House dogs served
100	as guard dogs. Others played with the Presidents' children.
109	And others clearly belonged to the Presidents and were
118	their personal four-legged friends. A few presidential
125	pooches were even as well known as their masters. Let's
135	take a look at some of the famous "First Dogs" of America. 147

Comprehension Check

1. Why might people vote for a candidate who has a dog as a pet? **Cause and Effect**

2. Why did the author write this passage about presidential dogs? **Author's Purpose**

	Words Read	–	Number of Errors	=	Words Correct Score
First Read		–		=	
Second Read		–		=	

TEKS 4.1 Read aloud grade-level stories with fluency and comprehension.

Name _____

> **Directions** tell the reader how to do something. They often include a list of materials and numbered steps to show the **sequence**, or order, in which things should be done. It is important to complete the steps from first to last.

Read the directions. Then answer the questions.

How to Wash a Dog

Materials: dog treat or toy, dog shampoo, tub, towels, water, bucket or hose

Directions:
Step 1: Before you begin, find a warm place to wash your dog.
Step 2: Fill a tub with four inches of warm water.
Step 3: Use a treat, a toy, or a friend to place the dog in the tub.
Step 4: Wet your dog's fur, and rub in the shampoo.
Step 5: Carefully use a bucket or hose to rinse your dog.
Step 6: Take the dog out of the tub. Pat the dog dry with a towel.
Step 7: Keep your dog out of the dirt until the dog is dry.

---

1. List three materials you need to give a dog a bath. _____

_____

2. What should you do before you fill the tub with water? _____

_____

3. How do you get the dog into the tub? _____

_____

4. What do you do after you rub shampoo into the dog's fur? _____

5. What may happen if you skip the last step? _____

_____

TEKS 4.13 (A) Determine the sequence of activities needed to carry out a procedure.

Dear Mrs. LaRue • **Grade 4/Unit 3**   **105**

Name _____

A **line graph** is a good way to show how something changes over time. Points on the graph are connected by lines that make it easy to tell whether the occurrences of something increased or decreased as time passed.

Look at the line graph below and answer the questions.

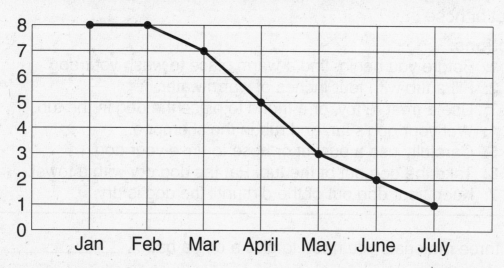

Number of Search Dog Requests in Vail, Colorado

1. During which two months were the largest number of search dogs needed? _____

2. How many search dogs were needed in May? _____

3. In which month were 5 search dogs needed? _____

4. Which two months had the same number of searches?

_____

5. How many more searches were requested in January than in July?

_____

© Macmillan/McGraw-Hill

TEKS 4.13 (B) Explain factual information presented graphically.

When you put the **prefix** *mis-* in front of a word, it changes the meaning of the word. *Mis-* means "badly" or "incorrectly" and derives from a German word meaning "go wrong."

Add the prefix *mis-* to each word. Then write a sentence with the new word.

New word

1. judge _____   4. read _____

2. spell _____   5. behave _____

3. treat _____

Sentence

1. _____

_____

2. _____

_____

3. _____

_____

4. _____

_____

5. _____

_____

TEKS **4.2 (A)** Determine the meaning of grade-level academic English words derived from other linguistic affixes.

Dear Mrs. LaRue • **Grade 4/Unit 3** **107**

A. Reading Strategy: Monitor and Adjust Comprehension

Make sure that you understand what you are reading. Forming scenes in your mind as you read will help you. Choose a text that you are reading this week, and complete the chart on a separate sheet of paper.

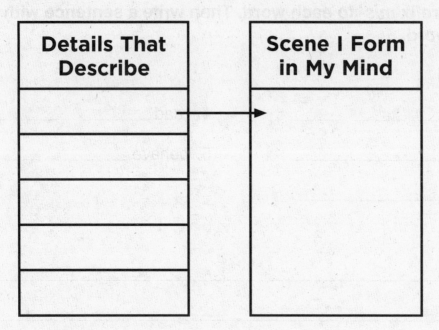

Details That Describe	Scene I Form in My Mind

B. Reading Strategy: Listening and Speaking

Choose something you would like to read. After reading, create a brief summary of the selection and present your summary to a partner. Be sure to state the main ideas or events clearly, maintaining meaning and logical order. Answer any questions from your partner with appropriate detail.

Then listen attentively as your partner presents his or her summary. Ask relevant questions and make pertinent comments.

TEKS **4.9** Read independently for a sustained period of time and paraphrase what the reading was about, maintaining meaning and logical order. **RC-4 (C)** Monitor and adjust comprehension.

When the letters **c** and **g** are followed by **e**, **i**, or **y**, they usually have a soft sound. Say the following words aloud.

ceiling	circus	cycle
genius	giant	gyroscope

Circle the word with soft c or g and write it on the line.

1. The young people were _____ their plan would work.

   careful   certain   cornered

2. They wanted to work in the _____.

   city   country   crowd

3. They could help people exercise in a _____.

   gymnasium   grade school   gang

4. Or they could give _____ care to sick pets.

   glad   grateful   gentle

5. Maybe they could feed the pets _____.

   cereal   corn   cupcakes

6. They could play with the _____ while they were not working.

   game   goose   gerbil

7. They could make sure the animals were free of _____.

   grease   gags   germs

8. Shelby has been learning to play the _____.

   clarinet   cymbals   castanets

dismiss	interact	motivate
conceived	definition	

A. From each pair of words below, circle the word that best completes the sentence. Then write the correct word on the line provided.

1. What is the (definition/interact) of the word *genius*? _____

2. Hearing the music of Louis Armstrong might (dismiss/motivate) you to

   play the trumpet. _____

3. When he played, Armstrong liked to (interact/motivate) with the people

   who watched him. _____

4. My sister and I (conceived/definition) of a way of playing like Louis

   Armstrong. _____

5. Mom will probably (dismiss/interact) our idea of starting a family band.

   _____

B. Write new sentences for three of the vocabulary words used above. Underline the vocabulary word in each sentence.

6. _____

7. _____

8. _____

© Macmillan/McGraw-Hill

TEKS **4.2 (B)** Use the context of the sentence to determine the meaning of unfamiliar words.

Name _____

> A **fact** is a statement that can be proven true.
> An **opinion** is a statement that tells someone's feelings or ideas.
> It cannot be proven true.
> Facts and opinions can appear together.

A. Read the following sentences. After each sentence write *fact* or *opinion*.

1. Our class went on a field trip to the art museum last week.

   _____

2. We saw one painting that was almost 500 years old. _____

3. It is harder to be a painter than to be a writer. _____

4. The best painters are from the United States. _____

5. Some painters study art in college. _____

6. Going to the art museum is a great way to spend an afternoon.

   _____

B. Write one fact about art. Then write one opinion about art.

7. Fact: _____

8. Opinion: _____

Name _____

As you read *Words Add Up to Success*, fill in the Fact and Opinion Chart.

Fact	Opinion

How does the information you wrote on this Fact and Opinion Chart help you better understand *Words Add Up to Success*?

TEKS 4.11 (B) Distinguish fact from opinion in a text.

As I read, I will pay attention to accuracy.

	Thousands of years ago in China, people made an
9	important discovery. They found out that caterpillars of
17	one kind of moth spin cocoons of silk. And better yet, they
29	found out that the cocoons could be unwound and the silk
40	thread could be woven into fabric.
46	Silk fabric is shiny. It is soft and smooth to the touch.
58	It is very light in weight. And it can be dyed in many
71	colors.
72	For thousands of years, the Chinese were the only
81	people who knew how to produce silk cloth. People in
91	other countries wanted to trade for the precious silk
100	fabric. Traders traveled to and from China on one
109	main road. They traded goods such as spices, glass,
118	and gold for silk. Sometimes they even traded horses
127	for silk. Over time, this route became known as the Silk
138	Road. 139

Comprehension Check

1. Are the statements in the second paragraph facts or opinions? **Main Idea and Details**

2. What is the main idea of the third paragraph? **Main Idea and Details**

	Words Read	–	Number of Errors	=	Words Correct Score
First Read		–		=	
Second Read		–		=	

TEKS 4.1 Read aloud grade-level stories with fluency and comprehension.

Words Add Up to Success
Grade 4/Unit 3   113

A **fact** is a statement that can be proved true. You can **verify**, or check, facts by using reliable sources. You can use encyclopedias, an atlas, biographies, textbooks, reliable Web sites, and other reference sources to check facts. An **opinion** is a statement that tells a person's feelings or beliefs. Unlike facts, opinions cannot be proved true.

A. Read the sentences. After each one, write fact or opinion.

1. Dogs make good pets. _____

2. Golden retrievers can weigh between 55 and 75 pounds. _____

3. Poodles are a type of dog. _____

4. Dogs are more fun to play with than cats. _____

B. Read the passage. Then complete the items.

Dogs are the best animals. They are fun playmates. They can also be trained to do many different helpful jobs. For example, some dogs are trained to help the police. Other dogs visit children in hospitals to help them get better. There are even some dogs that help guide people who are unable to see.

5. Write one opinion from the passage. _____

_____

6. Write one fact from the passage. _____

_____

7. How could you verify that this is a fact? _____

_____

© Macmillan/McGraw-Hill

TEKS **4.11 (B)** Distinguish fact from opinion in a text and explain how to verify what is a fact.

Name _____

The **Internet** is a collection of computer networks. A **search engine** reviews that collection to help you find information.

To use a search engine:
- Type a key word or a phrase in the Search box.
- The search engine will come back with a list of Web pages that contain the key words.
- When choosing a Web page, select trustworthy sources.

Use the Web page to answer the questions.

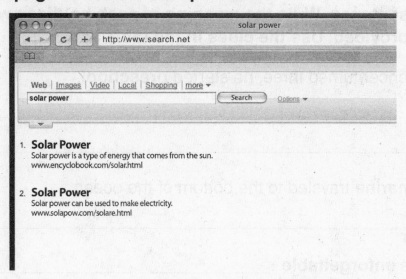

1. **What words have been entered in the search box?** _____

2. **If you clicked on the first Web page listed, what information would you find?** _____

3. **If you wanted to find information about solar power in California, what words would you put in the search box?** _____

4. **If you entered the word "California" in the search box, what information would you find?** _____

TEKS 4.24 (A) (ii) Collect information from online searches.

Words Add Up to Success
Grade 4/Unit 3   115

A **prefix** is a word part that is added to the beginning of a word to change its meaning. Many prefixes come from **Latin**, such as *pre-* and *sub-*. Others come from Greek or other languages. Understanding prefixes can help you figure out the meaning of a word.

Prefix	Meaning
pre-	before
sub-	under
un-	not

Read each sentence. Write the meaning of each boldface word on the line provided. Use the clues in the table above.

1. When Spencer turned three, he started **preschool**.

_____

_____

2. The **submarine** traveled to the bottom of the ocean.

_____

3. His face is **unforgettable**. _____

4. We rode the **subway** train in New York City.

_____

5. We went to a **preview** of the new movie.

_____

6. A new bike would be nice to have, but it is **unnecessary**.

_____

TEKS **4.2 (A)** Determine the meaning of grade-level academic English words derived from Latin, Greek, and other linguistic affixes.

A. Reading Strategy: Monitor and Adjust Comprehension

Make sure that you understand what you are reading. Rereading parts of a text will help you. Choose a text that you are reading this week, and complete the activity.

Pause after you read something that is hard to understand. Answer the question.

What is unclear about this part of the text? _____

_____

_____

Now reread that part of text. Reread more than once if needed. Then answer the question.

What does this part of the text mean? _____

_____

B. Independent Reading Log

Choose something you would like to read. After reading, complete the reading log. Be sure to paraphrase, or tell the main idea or meaning of the text. Keep the details or events in the correct order. You may use the log to talk to others about what you read.

Genre _____

Title _____

Author _____

This Text Is About _____

_____

_____

TEKS 4.9 Read independently for a sustained period of time and paraphrase what the reading was about, maintaining meaning and logical order.
RC-4 (C) Monitor and adjust comprehension.

Words Add Up to Success
Grade 4/Unit 3   117

Plurals are formed in the following ways:

- Most plural nouns end in **-s**.
- When a word ends in **-s, -ss, -sh, -ch,** or **-x, -es** is added.
- When a word ends in a **vowel** + **y, -s** is added.
- When a word ends in a **consonant** + **y**, the **y** is dropped and **-ies** is added.

Write the correct plural form of the underlined word on the line.

1. Many talented <u>artist</u> _____ have lived and worked in California.

2. Many of them study in <u>city</u> _____ such as Los Angeles and San Francisco.

3. The artist Ansel Adams took many <u>photo</u> _____ of the state.

4. His work showed high mountains and lush <u>valley</u> _____.

5. The state is home to many famous <u>writer</u> _____, too.

6. The writer Gary Soto writes about his childhood hopes and <u>wish</u>

_____.

7. He writes <u>story</u> _____ about his family.

8. Soto turns his <u>memory</u> _____ into art.

TEKS 3.1 (E) Monitor accuracy in decoding.

Name _____

| cranky | selfish | exasperated |
| specialty | famished | commotion |

Choose a vocabulary word from the list that has the opposite meaning of the word(s) in dark type and makes each sentence true. Write it on the line.

1. Mariel is **happy** because she slept for only four hours last night.

   _____

2. I had only a bag of peanuts for lunch, so I was **stuffed** by the time

   dinner came. _____

3. It would be **generous** not to share your lunch with a hungry friend.

   _____

4. My mom felt **pleased** when I forgot to take out the garbage for the

   fourth time. _____

5. Tyler's dog caused a **peaceful pause** when it escaped and ran through

   a grocery store. _____

Use one of the vocabulary words in a sentence of your own.

6. _____

TEKS **4.2 (B)** Use the context of the sentence to determine the meaning of unfamiliar words.

Ranita, The Frog Princess
Grade 4/Unit 3

119

Name _____

A **theme** is the lesson or message of a work of fiction. To identify
a story's message, look for clues in what the characters say and
do, what happens as the result of their actions, and how the
characters change.

**Read the fable. As you read, think about the theme. Then answer
the questions that follow.**

A fox fell in a deep hole. A goat walked by and stopped to ask what
the fox was doing. The fox replied, "A great drought will soon strike, and
I am down here drinking my fill. This hole is almost a desert. You better
come down, too, so you don't die of thirst."

Without thinking, the goat jumped into the hole. The fox quickly
scampered up the goat's back and horns and climbed out. Then he looked
down at the goat and said, "The next time someone tells you to do
something, look before you leap!"

1. Write two possible lessons you could learn from this story.

   • _____

   • _____

2. List two story events that support the lessons that you identified.

   • _____

   _____

   • _____

   _____

3. Explain how the lesson is the fable's theme.

   _____

   _____

© Macmillan/McGraw-Hill

TEKS **4.3 (A)** Summarize and explain the lesson or message of a work of
fiction as its theme.

Name _____

As you read *Ranita, The Frog Princess*, fill in the Theme Chart.

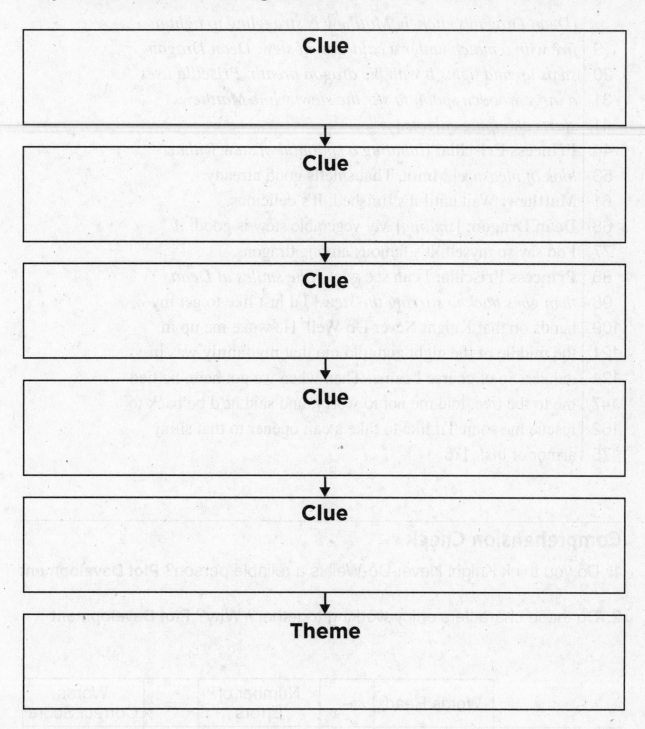

Clue

↓

Clue

↓

Clue

↓

Clue

↓

Clue

↓

Theme

How does the information you wrote in the Theme Chart help you understand *Ranita, The Frog Princess*?

TEKS **4.3 (A)** Summarize and explain the lesson or message of a work of fiction as its theme.

As I read, I will pay attention to expression.

	[*Dean Dragon's kitchen. Matthew is struggling to light a*
9	*fire with a match under a cauldron of stew. Dean Dragon*
20	*steps up and lights it with his dragon breath. Priscilla uses*
31	*a large wooden spoon to stir the stew, while Matthew*
41	*starts chopping carrots.*]
44	**Princess Priscilla:** [*inhaling a spoonful of stew with a*
53	*look of pleasure*] Mmm. That smells good already.
61	**Matthew:** Wait until it's finished. It's delicious.
68	**Dean Dragon:** [*smiling*] My vegetable stew is good, if
77	I do say so myself. It's famous among dragons.
86	**Princess Priscilla:** I can see why. [*She smiles at Dean,*
96	*then goes back to stirring the stew.*] I'd just like to get my
109	hands on that Knight Never-Do-Well. He woke me up in
121	the middle of the night and told me that my family was in
134	danger. So of course I came. Then when we got here, he tied
147	me to the tree, told me not to worry, and said he'd be back to
162	rescue me soon. I'd like to take a can opener to that shiny
175	armor of his. 178

Comprehension Check

1. Do you think Knight Never-Do-Well is a reliable person? **Plot Development**

2. Do these characters enjoy working together? Why? **Plot Development**

	Words Read	–	Number of Errors	=	Words Correct Score
First Read		–		=	
Second Read		–		=	

© Macmillan/McGraw-Hill

TEKS 4.1 Read aloud grade-level stories with fluency and comprehension.

> A **play** is a story told through **dialogue**, or characters speaking. Plays have special elements such as a list of **characters**, a description of the **setting**, and **stage directions** that describe the action and the setting. Action is divided into **scenes**.

Read this scene from a play. Then answer the questions.

Setting: A park in a large city in the summer

Characters: Tia, a sad little girl; Pilar, Tia's best friend; Tommy, Tia's brother; Mom, Tia's mother

SCENE 1

A girl, Tia, swings at the swing set alone with her head down.

TIA: *(sadly)* I can't believe everyone forgot my birthday. When Mom said that we were having a picnic, I thought it was a surprise party. But when we got here, there was no cake. No presents. Not even a card.

(Pilar enters.)

PILAR: *(excitedly)* Come on Tia, it's time for lunch!

(Tia gets up slowly and stands next to Pilar. She looks offstage and smiles.)

TOMMY: *(offstage)* Surprise!

1. According to the list of characters, who is Pilar? _____

2. What is the setting of the play? _____

_____

3. Based on the dialogue, why is Tia upset? _____

_____

4. What do the stage directions at the end of the scene tell you about Tia?

_____

TEKS 4.5 Describe the structural elements particular to dramatic literature.

Ranita, The Frog Princess
Grade 4/Unit 3   **123**

A **theme** is the lesson or message of a work of fiction. To identify the theme, look for clues in what the characters say and do, what happens because of their actions, and how the characters change.

Read the passage. As you read, think about the theme. Then answer the questions.

Once upon a time there was a man who had three daughters. The older daughters were very vain and selfish. The youngest, Cinderella, was a kind girl who loved animals. The father was going on a trip and said to his daughters, "What would you like me to bring you when I return?" The oldest demanded a fancy dress, the other, a fine hat. Cinderella said, "A little bird, please." Her sisters thought it was a silly request, but her father did as she asked and brought her a bird.

Later, the family was invited to a ball at the king's court. "See, Cinderella!" her oldest sister said. "If you had asked for a lovely dress, you could have come to the ball with us. You are so foolish!" When everyone had left, Cinderella's bird helped to make her beautiful. He gave her a flowing green dress, and so many diamonds that it blinded you to look at her. She went to the ball, and as soon as she entered the castle the king asked her to dance. They danced all night long, until the ball was almost over. "I need to get back home before my family notices I'm gone!" Cinderella cried. In her hurry, one of her slippers fell off outside the castle.

When she got home, Cinderella asked the bird to make her ugly again, but he would not obey. Just then there was a knock on the door. It was the king, and he was holding Cinderella's slipper. "It is you!" he cried. Cinderella's family came home just in time to see the king place the slipper on Cinderella's foot. Their mouths fell open in surprise, and they opened even wider when the king asked Cinderella to be his wife.

1. What is a possible theme for this story? _____

_____

2. On the lines below, list two story events that support that theme.

_____

TEKS **4.3 (A)** Summarize and explain the lesson or message of a work of fiction as its theme.

Analogies compare two pairs of words usually using **synonyms** or **antonyms**. For example, cranky is to mad as thin is to slim is an analogy using synonyms. Big is to little as short is to tall is an analogy using antonyms.

Read each analogy. Fill in the blank using a synonym or antonym.

1. *Truth* is to _____ as *hot* is to *cold*.

2. *Good* is to *bad* as *morning* is to _____.

3. *Careful* is to _____ as *up* is to *down*.

4. *Load* is to *fill* as *hit* is to _____.

5. _____ is to *found* as *happy* is to *sad*.

6. *Skip* is to *jump* as *speak* is to _____.

TEKS 4.2 (C) Complete analogies using knowledge of antonyms and synonyms.

Ranita, The Frog Princess
Grade 4/Unit 3   125

A. Reading Strategy: Monitor and Adjust Comprehension

Make sure that you understand what you are reading. Asking questions about a text will help you. Choose a text that you are reading this week, and complete the activity.

Pause after you read something that is hard to understand. Write a question about that part of the text.

Question: _____

_____

Now reread that part of the text or read further, looking for clues that help you answer your question. Write the answer.

Answer: _____

_____

Repeat as needed as you continue to read the text.

B. Independent Reading Log

Choose something you would like to read. After reading, complete the reading log. Be sure to paraphrase, or tell the main idea or meaning of the text. Keep the details or events in the correct order. You may use the log to talk to others about what you read.

Genre _____

Title _____

Author _____

This Text Is About _____

_____

_____

© Macmillan/McGraw-Hill

TEKS **4.9** Read independently for a sustained period of time and paraphrase what the reading was about, maintaining meaning and logical order.
RC-4 (C) Monitor and adjust comprehension.

Name _____

A **compound word** is made up of two short words. The two words together make a new word with a new meaning.

When I was at camp this summer, we built a campfire to keep warm at night.

camp + *fire* = *campfire*
camp: an outdoor place with tents or cabins
fire: the flame, heat, and light given off when wood burns
campfire: an outdoor fire for cooking or keeping warm in a camp

Draw a line dividing the two words that make up the compound word in each sentence. Then write the letter that matches the meaning of each word.

1. We had a bad snowstorm.	___ and ___	a. long, thin rope
2. Bentley loved snowflakes.	___ and ___	b. coming into being
3. Hail is made from raindrops.	___ and ___	c. small, thin, flat pieces
4. The child took the towels off the clothesline when the hail came.	___ and ___	d. plants with many long, thin leaves
		e. white crystals of ice
		f. what people wear
5. The child's birthday was in January.	___ and ___	g. windy, unsettled weather
		h. water from clouds
6. The grasshopper hid during the storm.	___ and ___	i. twenty-four hours
		j. small balls of something
		k. someone or something that jumps

© Macmillan/McGraw-Hill

strutting	swarms	barbecue
skyscrapers	glorious	collage

A. **Answer each question, substituting the vocabulary word for its underlined definition.**

1. Have you seen Jason? Why was he <u>walking in a proud manner</u> down the hall?

_____

2. Why were there <u>great numbers</u> of people at the mall?

_____

3. What kinds of food do you like to eat at an <u>outdoor gathering at which meat is roasted over an open fire and served</u>?

_____

4. Where can you go to see <u>very tall buildings</u>?

_____

5. What materials are you using to make that <u>artistic composition made by pasting or gluing materials together on a surface</u>?

_____

B. **Use two of the words above in one sentence.**

6. _____

TEKS **4.2 (B)** Use the context of the sentence to determine the meaning of unfamiliar words.

Name _____

The **characters** are the people who are in the story. A story
often describes the interaction of characters, including their
relationships and the changes they undergo. The **setting**
is when and where the story takes place. The **plot** is what
happens in the story, or the sequence of events.

Read the following passage. Then answer the questions that follow.

"I'm worried about art camp. I won't know anyone there," Brian said.

"Don't worry about it," his mom said. "You'll see. It'll be fine."

When Brian walked into the camp meeting room, he swallowed hard.
Most of the tables were full of kids talking and laughing with each other.
There was only one spot open, and it was at a table way in the back.

There were three other kids at the table—Alex, Kenya, and Mike. They
all knew each other, but they were happy to talk to Brian, too. Brian no
longer felt nervous. By the time he went home, he knew he had a new set
of friends for the summer.

1. What is the setting for this story? _____

2. Summarize the plot's main events in this story. _____

_____

_____

3. What kind of person is Brian in the beginning of the story? _____

_____

_____

4. How did Brian change at the end of the story? _____

_____

_____

TEKS 4.6 (A) Sequence and summarize the plot's main events.
4.6 (B) Describe the interaction of characters including the changes
they undergo.

Me and Uncle Romie 129
Grade 4/Unit 3

Name _____

As you read *Me and Uncle Romie*, fill in the Story Flowchart.

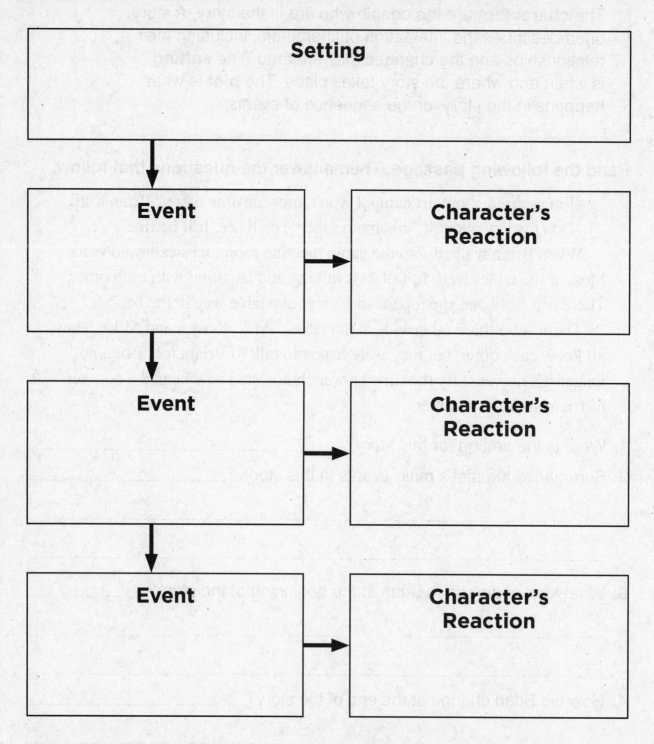

Setting

Event → **Character's Reaction**

Event → **Character's Reaction**

Event → **Character's Reaction**

How does the information you wrote in the Story Flowchart help you monitor your comprehension of *Me and Uncle Romie*?

© Macmillan/McGraw-Hill

TEKS **4.6 (A)** Sequence and summarize the plot's main events and explain their influence on future events. **4.6 (B)** Describe the interaction of characters including their relationships and the changes they undergo.

Name _____

As I read, I will pay attention to my reading rate in order to match the action in the story.

	Carly held her breath as the broad-tailed hummingbird
8	fluttered near the cluster of wildflowers. She stared into
17	her camera, waiting. A fly landed on Carly's arm. She
27	flicked it away with a finger. The bird flew near a flower.
39	The flower wasn't red enough, though. Carly waited.
47	The bird flew to another flower. This one was too small.
58	Finally, the bird hesitated over the largest, reddest flower.
67	Carly began to snap pictures. She was certain that these
77	would be some of the best pictures she had ever taken.
88	Carly raced home and uploaded the pictures onto her
97	computer. She couldn't wait to see the results.
105	But when the pictures came up on the screen, she was
116	disappointed. Carly studied them, then opened her photo
124	journal. She wrote: "Hummingbird pictures: The bird's
131	wings are a blur, not enough detail on flower, bird isn't
142	close enough to the flower in any shot. Why aren't these
153	the way I thought they would be?" 160

Comprehension Check

1. What do you learn about Carly in this passage? **Plot Development**

2. How might the journal help Carly take better pictures in the future? **Plot Development**

	Words Read	–	Number of Errors	=	Words Correct Score
First Read		–		=	
Second Read		–		=	

© Macmillan/McGraw-Hill

TEKS 4.1 Read aloud grade-level stories with fluency and comprehension.

Me and Uncle Romie   131
Grade 4/Unit 3

Before writing and sending a letter, you must decide whether a formal letter or an informal e-mail is better for your **audience and purpose**. All letters have three basic parts: a **salutation**, or greeting; a **body**, or the main message; and the **complimentary closing**, or the line above the letter writer's name.

Read the letters. Label the salutation, the body, and the closing of each letter. Then answer the questions.

To: Linda227@freemail.com
From: Katiebird@freemail.com
Subject: Thanks!

Hey Linda!

Thank you so much for the shirt you got me for my birthday. I love it! Are we still going to the movie on Friday?

Always,
Katie

Sanchez Sports Store
24 Third St.
Austin, TX 78705

Dear Mr. Sanchez,

Thank you for giving to our school's canned food drive. We could not have met our goal without you.

Sincerely,
Katie Martin

1. How are the e-mail and the thank-you letter appropriate for their audiences and purposes? _____

_____

_____

2. Compare and contrast the e-mail and the thank-you letter. _____

_____

_____

Write a letter inviting your friends to a special event.

TEKS **4.14 (C)** Compare various written conventions used for digital media.
4.18 (B) Write letters whose language is tailored to the audience and purpose and that use appropriate conventions.

© Macmillan/McGraw-Hill

Directions explain how to do something. Sometimes numbered steps are given to tell the reader the order in which things should be done. **Sequence words**, such as *first, then, next,* and *last*, can also help readers follow directions. Sometimes a list of needed **materials** is included in the directions.

Read the following directions. Then answer the questions.

How to Paint a Room

Materials

paint	drop cloth	paint stirrer	roller
painter's tape	paintbrushes	paint tray	

Directions

1. Put drop cloths on the floor and furniture to protect them.
2. Place blue painter's tape around the areas that you do not want painted, like windows, for instance.
3. Open the paint cans and mix the paint with a stirrer.
4. Pour the paint into a paint tray. Use a roller to paint the walls.
5. Use a paintbrush to paint the corners, edges, and other spots the roller can't reach.
6. When you are finished, wash the brushes and rollers with warm water.

1. How many materials are needed to paint a room? ____

2. What is the first thing you should do before you paint a room?

_____

3. What do you pour the paint into? _____

4. What would happen if you skipped Step 2?

_____

TEKS 4.13 (A) Determine the sequence of activities needed to carry out a procedure.

Me and Uncle Romie
Grade 4/Unit 3   **133**

Name _____

> **Context clues** can help readers determine the meaning of
> an unfamiliar word. Sometimes writers use **definitions** or
> **examples** to help readers define unfamiliar words.

A. Underline the context clues that describe the meaning of the boldfaced word. Then write the word's definition.

1. We decided that the **theme** of our collage would be what we did during our vacation.

   Definition: _____

2. The chef felt her masterpiece was not complete until she **shredded** cheese into tiny strips and sprinkled it on top of the omelette.

   Definition: _____

3. My neighbor offered me the **proposition** of getting $20 each time it snows for shoveling his stairs and sidewalk.

   Definition: _____

B. On the lines below, write an example that is a context clue for the boldfaced word.

4. The **skyscraper**, such as _____, towers above the rest of the city.

5. The biologist studied a **protozoan**, including _____, under the microscope.

6. The artist used chalk, _____, and other **materials** to create her artwork.

TEKS **4.2 (B)** Use the context of the sentence to determine the meaning of unfamiliar words.

Name _____

A. Reading Strategy: Monitor and Adjust Comprehension

Make sure that you understand what you are reading. Using what you know, forming scenes in your mind, rereading, and asking questions will help you. Choose a text that you are reading this week, and answer the questions.

Which part of the text is unclear? _____

_____

What is unclear about it? _____

_____

_____

Which strategy can you use to understand it? _____

_____

B. Independent Reading Log

Choose something you would like to read. After reading, complete the reading log. Be sure to paraphrase, or tell the main idea or meaning of the text. Keep the details or events in the correct order. You may use the log to talk to others about what you read.

Genre_____

Title _____

Author _____

This Text Is About _____

_____

_____

TEKS **4.9** Read independently for a sustained period of time and paraphrase what the reading was about, maintaining meaning and logical order.
RC-4 (C) Monitor and adjust comprehension.

Me and Uncle Romie   **135**
Grade 4/Unit 3

When you add **-ed** or **-ing** to a word, sometimes you have to add or drop a letter before adding the ending.
- If the word has a short vowel sound and ends in a single consonant, double the last letter before adding the ending.
- If the word ends in **e**, drop the **e** before adding the ending.

A. Complete the table by writing the correct -ed and -ing forms of each of these words.

Base Word	Word + *ing*	Word + *ed*
1. hop	_____	_____
2. hope	_____	_____
3. flip	_____	_____
4. force	_____	_____
5. tap	_____	_____
6. tape	_____	_____

B. Write four sentences, each using one of the words above.

7. _____

8. _____

9. _____

10. _____

© Macmillan/McGraw-Hill

TEKS 3.1 (E) Monitor accuracy in decoding.

Name _____

eavesdropping	route	logical
jumble	scornfully	acquaintance

Answer the questions using a vocabulary word that means the same as the underlined word or phrase.

1. Did the raccoon leave a <u>big mess</u> when it turned over the garbage can?

_____

2. Is this the most direct <u>way</u> to get to the lake?

_____

3. Was the owl in the tree <u>listening in</u> on your conversation by the campfire?

_____

4. Is it <u>reasonable</u> to expect an animal to act like a person?

_____

5. What person did you <u>have the pleasure of meeting</u>?

_____

6. Would an owl look at a wolf with <u>dislike and disrespect</u>?

_____

© Macmillan/McGraw-Hill

TEKS 4.2 (B) Use the context of the sentence to determine the meaning of unfamiliar words.

The Cricket in Times Square
Grade 4/Unit 4
137

A **theme** is the lesson or message of a work of fiction. To identify a story's message, look for clues in what the characters say and do, what happens as the result of their actions, and how the characters change.

Read the passage. As you read, think about the theme. Then answer the questions that follow.

Mario Mouse did not always do as he was told. His mother had told him never to leave the safety of their mouse hole, because the world outside was dangerous. But Mario was an adventurous mouse. One evening he ran out of the hole to see the world.

My, the world was big! He found himself in a huge room. It had chairs, a couch, and low tables. In one corner, he saw a big box that had bright pictures and spoke! Mario crept forward to look at the bright pictures.

Just then, a big furry animal bounded into the room, making snarling noises. Mario was terrified. He let out a squeak and scurried back to his mouse hole. He dove through it, back to safety. "Mom was so right," he thought.

1. What is one of the themes of this story? _____

_____

_____

2. On the lines below, list three story events that support the theme that you identified.

a. _____

b. _____

c. _____

TEKS 4.3 (A) Summarize and explain the lesson or message of a work of fiction as its theme.

Name _____

As you read *The Cricket in Times Square*, fill in the Theme Chart.

Clue

↓

Clue

↓

Clue

↓

Clue

↓

Clue

↓

Theme

How does the information you wrote in the Theme Chart help you to better understand *The Cricket in Times Square*?

TEKS **4.3 (A)** Summarize and explain the lesson or message of a work of fiction as its theme.

Name _____

As I read, I will pay attention to intonation and expression.

	Stripes raised his eyes and blinked at Jani. He was a lovely
12	striped cat. Jani thought he looked like a little tiger. She picked
24	the cat up. She sat with him on a chair, stroking his head.
37	"You'll never believe what we learned in school today," she
47	told Stripes.
49	Stripes looked up at her with wise green eyes. "People used
60	to make leopard-skin coats," she told him. "Some people still
71	do. A coat made from a cat, Stripes. It makes me so mad!"
84	Jani could not be sure, but she thought that Stripes scrunched
95	up his nose in disgust.
100	That night, Jani fell into a restless sleep. She tossed and
111	turned. She dreamed about animals who could talk. In her
121	dream, she hid nearby, **eavesdropping** on their conversation.
129	The animals were in danger. And they needed help. Suddenly
139	she woke up. It was almost midnight, but there was a light in
152	her room. "Who's there?" she asked. 158

Comprehension Check

1. Why does Jani fall into a restless sleep? **Plot**

2. Why might Jani feel sympathy for leopards? **Cause and Effect**

	Words Read	–	Number of Errors	=	Words Correct Score
First Read		–		=	
Second Read		–		=	

© Macmillan/McGraw-Hill

TEKS 4.1 Read aloud grade-level stories with fluency and comprehension.

Name _____

When you read persuasive writing, try to determine the **author's point of view**, or what he or she believes. In persuasive writing, an author uses **persuasive language** to influence readers to agree with his or her point of view. Watch for positive and negative language that appeals to your emotions.

Read the passage below. Then complete the items that follow.

Some people like living in big cities. I think it is best to live in the country. Cities are too noisy and crowded. Life in the country is quiet and peaceful. If you like nature, the country is the place for you. The country is beautiful! In the country, trees and flowers are everywhere. In cities, you are trapped by buildings, sidewalks, and streets. You have to go to a park to find trees and flowers. Many people who live in cities have dogs and cats as pets. However, if you live in the country, you can raise all kinds of animals. You might even be able to have a horse! For all these reasons and many more, I think country life is definitely better than city life.

1. What is the author's point of view? _____

_____

2. Circle three examples of positive language. Underline three examples of negative language.

3. How does the author use positive and negative language to influence the

reader? _____

_____

_____

_____

TEKS 4.12 Explain how an author uses language to present information to influence what the reader thinks or does.

The Cricket in Times Square
Grade 4/Unit 4   141

Advertisements use pictures and text to influence people to buy or do something. Advertisements use several techniques of persuasion:
- loaded language, such as *best*, *better*, and *special*
- bandwagon, or urging that you join many other people
- testimonials, or the backing of a celebrity
- warnings that the offer is good for a limited time only

Read each advertisement. Then answer the questions.

Our world-class bird feeder will blow you away! It's the best there is. As Bob Wells of the Nature Channel says, "You won't find a better feeder anywhere."

1. What techniques does the advertisement use? _____

2. What words or phrases did you use to figure out the advertisement's

   approach? _____

Join your friends and neighbors by donating to the Save the Tigers fund. Act now and receive this beautiful tote bag.

3. What techniques does the advertisement use? _____

4. What words or phrases did you use to figure out the advertisement's

   approach? _____

TEKS **4.12** Explain how an author uses language to present information to influence what the reader thinks or does.

© Macmillan/McGraw-Hill

Name _____

Context clues are words in the same or surrounding sentences that help a reader determine or clarify the meaning of an unfamiliar word.

Read the paragraph below. Then write the meaning of each word in dark type and the context clues that helped you figure it out.

The **audience streamed** into the theater to hear Regina Jackson's talk. Hundreds of people moved smoothly but quickly into their seats. Jackson was the world's leading **authority** on **jaguars**. No one else knew more than she did about the lives of these big cats. From the moment she began to speak, everyone sat quietly. You could see by their interested expressions that they were **fascinated** by what she had to say. When Regina finished, everyone stood up and began to applaud.

1. audience   Definition: _____

Context clues: _____

2. streamed   Definition: _____

Context clues: _____

3. authority   Definition: _____

Context clues: _____

4. jaguars   Definition: _____

Context clues: _____

5. fascinated   Definition: _____

Context clues: _____

TEKS **4.2 (B)** Use the context of the sentence to determine the meaning of unfamiliar words.

Name _____

A. Reading Strategy: Make Inferences

Making inferences will help you understand what you read. Keep in mind that you should support every inference with details from the text. Choose a text that you are reading this week, and answer the questions.

What question do you have that is not answered in the text?

_____

What knowledge do you have that might help you answer the question?

_____

_____

What clues from the text might help you answer the question?

_____

_____

What inference can you make to answer the question?

_____

_____

B. Independent Reading Log

Choose something you would like to read. After reading, complete the reading log. Be sure to paraphrase, or tell the main idea or meaning of the text. Keep the details or events in the correct order. You may use the log to talk to others about what you read.

Genre _____

Title _____

Author _____

This Text Is About _____

_____

TEKS **4.9** Read independently for a sustained period of time and paraphrase what the reading was about, maintaining meaning and logical order.
RC-4 (D) Make inferences about text and use textual evidence to support understanding.

When words end in a consonant + **y**, you do two things to add endings like **-er** or **-ed**. First you change the **y** to **i**. Then you add the ending.

A. Change y to i and add the indicated ending to each word. Then write the new word in the blank.

lazy + er   1. _____

reply + ed   2. _____

worry + es   3. _____

happy + est   4. _____

empty + er   5. _____

family + es   6. _____

dizzy + est   7. _____

funny + er   8. _____

B. Follow the model and write four more words.

9. _____   _____

10. _____   _____

11. _____   _____

12. _____   _____

© Macmillan/McGraw-Hill

territory	investigates	solitary
prehistoric	nutrients	communication

Read each sentence and decide whether it is true or false. If it is true, write True. If it is false, write False, and explain why.

1. An ant *investigates* new discoveries of food with its antennae.

_____

2. Ants guard the *territory* in which they live.

_____

3. Ants are not *prehistoric* creatures because they've been around for only about 500 years.

_____

4. Some insects are *solitary*, which means they like living in groups.

_____

5. Like ants, we get our *nutrients* from the foods we eat.

_____

6. Ants use *communication* to tell each other where to find food.

_____

TEKS **4.2 (B)** Use the context of the sentence to determine the meaning of unfamiliar words.

When using **description**, an author defines, categorizes, or classifies information by describing its qualities or characteristics. To identify description, look for facts and details that are organized into sections or groupings.

Read the passage. Then answer the questions that follow.

The Life Cycle of the Ant

Egg

Ants begin life as tiny white or yellowish eggs. The eggs are oval in shape and less than 1/16 of an inch long. They hatch in two-to-six weeks.

Larva

Larvae look like small, white worms. They don't have legs, and they can't move much. They grow for several weeks to several months. Larvae shed their skin over and over as they grow.

Pupa

During this stage, the ants change into their adult bodies. In the end, they look like white ants. Their legs and antennae are snug against their bodies. After this stage, they are full-grown.

1. Write the names of the main sections of this passage.

_____

2. Write two details from the first section.

_____

3. Write two details from the second section.

_____

_____

TEKS 5.11 (C) Analyze how the organizational pattern of a text influences the relationships among the ideas.

The Life and Times of the Ant
Grade 4/Unit 4   147

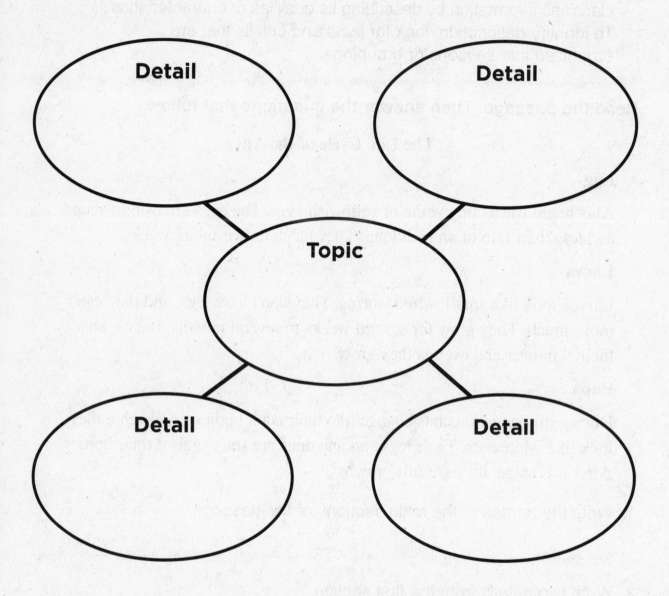

Name _____

As you read *The Life and Times of the Ant*, fill in the
Description Web.

Detail

Detail

Topic

Detail

Detail

How does completing the Description Web help you answer questions
about how ants behave in *The Life and Times of the Ant*?

TEKS **5.11 (C)** Analyze how the organizational pattern of a text influences the
relationships among the ideas.

As I read, I will pay attention to my reading rate.

	Did you know that only the male cricket sings? A
10	male cricket sings to attract a female cricket. This cricket
20	**communication** is made when the male cricket scrapes
28	its front wings together. Each wing has a sharp edge and
39	a bumpy part like a file. First, the cricket lifts its wings.
51	Then, it rubs the sharp edge of one wing against the file
63	of the other. It is almost as if it is playing a violin. Each
77	type of cricket has a different song.
84	Crickets don't have very good eyesight. They depend
92	on their hearing. But their ears aren't on their heads.
102	Crickets have ears on their front legs. Each ear is a small
114	hole with a thin covering.
119	A long time ago, house crickets could be found near
129	warm kitchen stoves. The crickets fed on crumbs that had
139	fallen from the stove. They would also sit near the warm
150	fireplace that heated the home. People often felt comforted
159	by listening to the chirping crickets on cold nights. Today
169	crickets inside homes must find a warm place to hide. 179

Comprehension Check

1. Describe crickets' ears. **Main Idea and Details**

2. Compare how crickets could live in houses in the past and today. **Compare and Contrast**

	Words Read	–	Number of Errors	=	Words Correct Score
First Read		–		=	
Second Read		–		=	

© Macmillan/McGraw-Hill

TEKS 4.1 Read aloud grade-level stories with fluency and comprehension.

The Life and Times of the Ant

Name _____

Procedural texts such as **directions** tell the reader how to do something. Directions usually include a list of **materials** and numbered steps that show the order in which things should be done. Procedural texts may also include information presented in **graphic features** such as maps, diagrams, and illustrations.

Read the directions below. Then answer the questions that follow.

How to Make an Ant Farm

Materials: large jar, cardboard tube, soil, sand, ants, cloth, rubber band, and bits of food

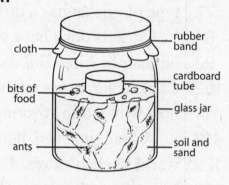

Step 1: Place a cardboard tube inside a large jar. The tube makes the ants tunnel near the side of the jar so that you can see them.

Step 2: Fill the jar with soil and sand.

Step 3: Find an ant colony in your yard or a park. Catch at least 20 ants from the same colony to put in your farm.

Step 4: Try to find a queen ant. Queen ants are usually larger than the other ants. Some queen ants have wings.

Step 5: After you place the ants in the jar, cover the top with cloth. Use a rubber band to hold the cloth in place.

Step 6: Feed the ants once a week. Ants can eat tiny bits of food.

1. What does this procedural text tell the reader?

_____

_____

2. What should you do after you fill the jar with soil and sand?

_____

3. Look at the diagram of the ant farm. Why is it important to cover the ant

farm with cloth? _____

_____

_____

TEKS 4.13 **(B)** Explain factual information presented graphically.

Name _____

A **fable** is a short story that teaches a lesson. The **moral** is the lesson that is taught. Fables often have animal characters that behave like people. This is called **personification**, a literary device that gives human characteristics to animals or objects.

Read each fable and answer the questions.

A fire ant fell into a river and started to panic. A dove saw this happen, plucked a leaf from a tree, and dropped it near the ant. The ant climbed on the leaf and got safely to shore. "Thank you," said the ant. "I wish I could repay you for your help." The dove waved her wing and flew away. Soon after, a hunter came by and aimed at the dove. The ant ran up to the hunter and stung him on the foot. The hunter missed his target.

1. Write an example of personification from the story.

_____

2. What might the moral of this fable be?

_____

A crow was very thirsty. He found a pitcher and said, "Wow, this water looks really good!" He tried to drink from the pitcher but couldn't reach the water. Then, he started dropping pebbles into the pitcher. With each pebble, the water rose higher until, at last, it rose high enough for him to drink.

3. Write an example of personification from the story.

_____

4. What do you think the moral of this story is?

_____

TEKS 4.3 (A) Summarize the lesson or message of a work of fiction as its theme.

The Life and Times of the Ant
Grade 4/Unit 4   151

Words in English come from many sources. For example, the word *life* comes from the German word *leib*, meaning "body." Many words come from Latin and Greek. English words often have **Latin** or **Greek Roots**. Knowing the meaning of common Latin and Greek roots can help you figure out the meanings of many words.

Latin Roots		**Greek Roots**	
act- = do	*migr-* = move	*astro-* = star	*tele-* = far
aud- = hear	*urb-* = city	*bio-* = life	*therm-* = heat

A. Look at each word and identify the root. Circle the Latin roots and underline the Greek roots.

1. astronomer

2. immigrant

3. telephone

4. biologist

5. audience

6. action

B. Write the meaning of the word. Use a dictionary, if necessary.

7. thermostat

_____

8. urban

_____

TEKS **4.2 (A)** Determine the meaning of grade-level academic English words derived from Latin, Greek, or other linguistic roots.

A. Reading Strategy: Make Inferences

Making inferences will help you understand what you read. Keep in mind that you should support every inference with details from the text. Choose a text that you are reading this week, and complete the chart on a separate sheet of paper.

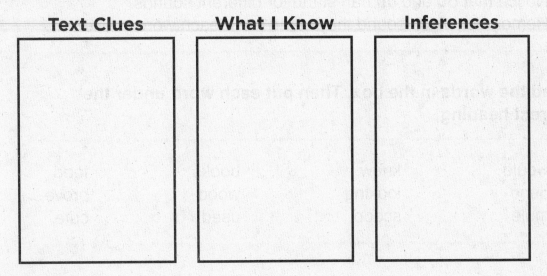

Text Clues	What I Know	Inferences

B. Book Talk

Choose something you would like to read. Afterward, participate in a teacher-led discussion about the selections that you and your classmates read. You should

- answer questions from your teacher and classmates with appropriate detail.

- pose questions about other students' reading with appropriate detail.

- provide suggestions that build upon the ideas of others.

TEKS 4.9 Read independently for a sustained period of time.
RC-4 (D) Make inferences about text and use textual evidence to support understanding.

The Life and Times of the Ant **153**
Grade 4/Unit 4

Name _____

- Words like **sp<u>oo</u>l**, **gr<u>ew</u>**, **m<u>o</u>ve**, **s<u>ou</u>p**, and **s<u>ui</u>t** have the /ü/ sound.
- Words like **br<u>oo</u>ks** and **sh<u>ou</u>ld** have the /ů/ sound.
- Words like **c<u>u</u>bes** and **m<u>u</u>le** have the /ū/ sound.

Notice that **oo** and **ou** can stand for different sounds.
Remember which sound they stand for in each word you learn.

Read the words in the box. Then put each word under the correct heading.

would	knew	books	food
dune	looking	wood	prove
mule	scoop	used	cute

/ü/	/ů/	/ū/
_____	_____	_____
_____	_____	_____
_____	_____	_____
_____	_____	_____
_____	_____	_____

TEKS 3.1 (E) Monitor accuracy in decoding.

| electrical | globe | fuels | decayed |

A. Write the vocabulary word that completes each sentence on the line.

1. Countries from around the _____ will participate in the conference.

2. _____ leaves and grass help new plants to grow.

3. _____ are substances, such as wood, coal, and oil, that are burned to make heat and power.

4. Many things that we use everyday are _____ , such as computers, telephones, and lighting.

B. Now, write a paragraph in which you use each vocabulary word at least once.

_____

_____

_____

_____

_____

_____

TEKS 4.2 (B) Use the context of the sentence to determine the meaning of unfamiliar words.

The Power of Oil • **Grade 4/Unit 4**   155

Name _____

> An **author's purpose** for writing is usually to **entertain**, to **inform**, or to **persuade**. Sometimes the author states the purpose directly. At other times the purpose is implied.

Read each situation below. Then, write the author's purpose on the line provided: to entertain, to inform, or to persuade.

1. A journalist writes about a mentoring program at the local high school.

   _____

2. An author writes a short story about a boy and his mentor.

   _____

3. The mayor gives a speech asking people to join a new mentoring program.

   _____

4. A person writes a guidebook to train youth mentors.

   _____

5. A volunteer makes a poster that tells workers about a night school opportunity.

   _____

   Is the purpose for the poster stated directly or implied? Explain your answer.

   _____

   _____

   _____

TEKS **4.10** Explain the difference between a stated and an implied purpose for an expository text.

Name _____

As you read *The Power of Oil*, fill in the Author's Purpose Map.

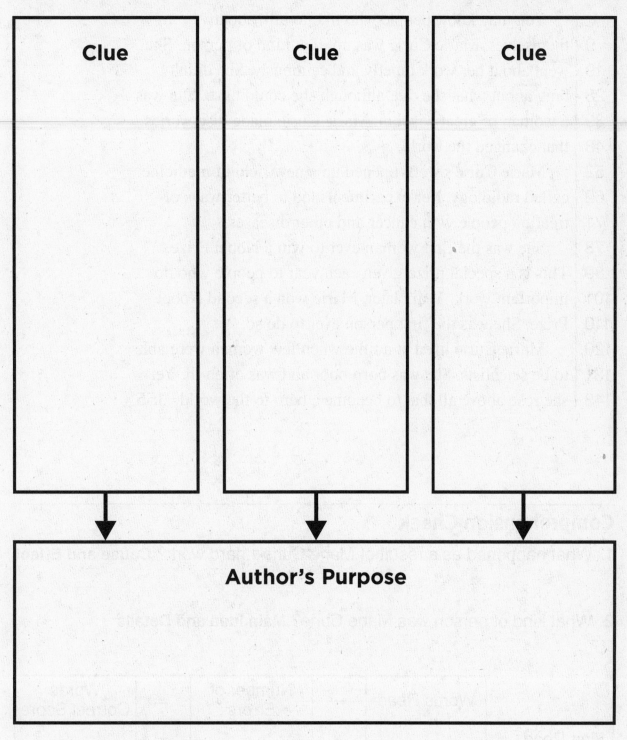

Clue	Clue	Clue

Author's Purpose

How does the information you wrote on this Author's Purpose Map help you answer questions about *The Power of Oil*?

TEKS **4.10** Explain the difference between a stated and an implied purpose for an expository text.

Name _____

As I read, I will pay attention to my accuracy.

	You may know people who like to talk about
9	themselves. Marie Curie was not that kind of person. She
19	went about her work quietly and cautiously. She didn't
28	brag about what she did, although she could have. She was
39	a woman of great wisdom. Marie Curie made discoveries
48	that changed the world.
52	Marie Curie's work opened up a new field of medicine
62	called radiology. Her experiments led to better ways of
71	treating people with cancer and other diseases.
78	She was the first woman ever to win a Nobel Prize.
89	This is a special prize given each year to people who do
101	important work. Years later, Marie won a second Nobel
110	Prize. She was the first person ever to do so.
120	Marie Curie lived at a time when few women were able
131	to be scientists. She was born poor and was often ill. Yet
143	she rose above all that to become a hero to the world. 155

Comprehension Check

1. What happened as a result of Marie Curie's hard work? **Cause and Effect**

2. What kind of person was Marie Curie? **Main Idea and Details**

	Words Read	–	Number of Errors	=	Words Correct Score
First Read		–		=	
Second Read		–		=	

TEKS 4.1 Read aloud grade-level stories with fluency and comprehension.

Use a variety of strategies to **monitor and adjust comprehension** as you read. Create **sensory images** in your mind by using the story's descriptive details to help you imagine the characters, settings, and action. **Ask questions** as you read, and answer them to improve your understanding. **Rereading** the story aloud also helps your understanding.

Read the story. Then complete the items that follow.

Tara's brown eyes were wide as she looked out the bus window at the tall buildings. Her class was on its way to the art museum. Tara had never been to an art museum before. She tapped her foot nervously with excitement. The bus stopped in front of a very large stone building. Tara gasped. The art museum was huge! Tara imagined all the beautiful paintings inside the building. She smiled happily and jumped out of her seat. She could not wait to go inside. She knew that this was going to be a fun day.

1. Which details in the story help you create an image of Tara?

_____

2. What details in the story help you create an image of the setting?

_____

3. Write and answer a question about something that happens in the story.

_____

_____

4. Write and answer a question about Tara's feelings in the story.

_____

_____

5. Reread the story aloud. In what ways does rereading the story help you understand it better? _____

_____

When you **skim,** you look quickly through a selection to find out what it is about. You look for its main idea and important details.

When you **scan,** you run your eyes through a text looking for a specific word or phrase. You don't read every word.

Read the information below. Then answer the questions that follow.

How to Scan for Information

When you scan for information, follow these steps.

- Identify the key words and phrases that you are looking for.
- Pass your eyes over each line of print quickly.
- Don't stop until you see your key word or phrase.
- Double-check to be sure that you have found the information.

1. Why would it not have been useful to skim the passage in the box?

_____

_____

_____

2. If you're looking for key words and phrases, are you skimming or

scanning? _____

3. Which of the following is the best key word or phrase that you would use for scanning?
   a. The Great Wall   **b.** murals   **c.** painting

4. Which do you think is more useful, skimming or scanning? Explain your

answer. _____

_____

TEKS **4.11 (D)** Use multiple text features to gain an overview of the contents of text and to locate information. **4.24 (B)** Use skimming and scanning techniques to identify data by looking at text features.

Name _____

When you're reading, you may find words that you do not know. When this happens, look in the text for **context clues**. You may find words and phrases that give you the **definition** of an unfamiliar word.

Read each sentence. In your own words, write the definition of each underlined word on the line. Circle the context clues that helped you determine the word's meaning.

1. We spun the <u>globe</u> of the world, looking for the countries of Africa.

   _____

2. He unplugged TVs, refrigerators, and other <u>electrical</u> appliances that

   use electricity. _____

3. Do your parents use several <u>fuels</u> as sources of energy to heat your home?

   _____

4. Since the animals' remains had <u>decayed</u>, they had broken down to the

   point that we couldn't tell what they were. _____

TEKS 4.2 (B) Use the context of the sentence to determine the meaning of unfamiliar words.

The Power of Oil • Grade 4/Unit 4   161

A. Reading Strategy: Make Inferences

Making inferences will help you understand what you read. Keep in mind that you should support every inference with details from the text. Choose a text that you are reading this week, and complete the web.

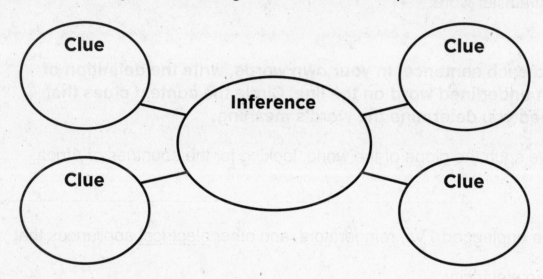

B. Independent Reading Log

Choose something you would like to read. After reading, complete the reading log. Be sure to paraphrase, or tell the main idea or meaning of the text. Keep the details or events in the correct order. You may use the log to talk to others about what you read.

Genre_____

Title_____

Author_____

This Text Is About _____

_____

_____

_____

© Macmillan/McGraw-Hill

TEKS **4.9** Read independently for a sustained period of time and paraphrase what the reading was about, maintaining meaning and logical order. **RC-4 (D)** Make inferences about text and use textual evidence to support understanding.

Name _____

The /oi/ sound can be spelled with **oi** as in **foil** or with **oy** as in **boy**. The /ou/ sound can be spelled with **ou** as in **couch** or with **ow** as in **now**. Keep in mind, though, that not all words containing **oi** have the /oi/ sound and not all words spelled with **ou** and **ow** have the /ou/ sound.

In each row of words below, there is one word that does not belong. If the word does not have the same sound as the others, make an X over it. Then, write /oi/ or /ou/ on the blank line to describe the sound in the three remaining words.

1. joy   foil   employ   onion   _____

2. coil   destroy   oil   going   _____

3. mouth   doubt   through   how   _____

4. broil   doing   spoil   noise   _____

5. couch   dough   cloud   crowd   _____

6. enjoy   soil   shooing   toys   _____

7. now   enough   crown   proud   _____

8. brow   cow   low   down   _____

9. annoy   voices   boil   porpoise   _____

10. thought   shower   loud   trout   _____

| anticipation | enormous | released |
| encouraged | glanced | slender |

Write a vocabulary word to complete each sentence.

1. When the team _____ its grip on the rope, the other team fell to the ground.

2. The chef cut the chicken into _____ slices.

3. There are many types of animals that are _____, such as whales, elephants, and giraffes.

4. The little boy waited in _____ for his turn to get on the ride.

5. The reporter briefly _____ at his notes before the interview.

6. The students were _____ to keep striving for their goals.

TEKS **4.2 (B)** Use the context of the sentence to determine the meaning of unfamiliar words.

© Macmillan/McGraw-Hill

Name _____

When you **draw conclusions**, you use information from the selection and your own prior experience connected to the reading selection.

Read the paragraph and answer the questions below.

Will stopped for several seconds and glanced around at his friends and neighbors. Many were shoveling sand into plastic bags. Others were carrying the heavy bags and piling them into a wide row along the riverbank to keep the rising water from spilling into the streets. The water had already destroyed some stores along Main Street. He feared that his dad's auto repair shop might have been one of them. Everyone was working frantically because the water was rising quickly, and it was getting dark. All Will wanted to do was change into dry clothes and sleep for hours, but he grabbed a shovel and started back to work.

1. What text clues help you draw a conclusion about where Will is? _____

_____

2. What conclusion can you draw about where Will is? _____

_____

3. What text clues help you draw a conclusion that Will is helping other

characters? _____

_____

4. What text clues help you draw a conclusion about how Will is feeling?

_____

5. What conclusion can you draw about how Will is feeling? _____

_____

TEKS **4.6 (B)** Describe the interaction of characters including their relationships and the changes they undergo.

Ima and the Great Texas Ostrich
Race • Grade 4/Unit 4

As you read *Ima and the Great Texas Ostrich Race*, fill in the
Conclusions Chart.

Text Clues	Conclusion

How does the information you wrote in the Conclusions Chart help
you understand *Ima and the Great Texas Ostrich Race*?

TEKS 4.6 (B) Describe the interaction of characters including their
relationships and the changes they undergo.

Name _____

As I read, I will pay attention to reading with expression.

	The Hoover Dam brought the Colorado River under
8	control. The dam also created a reserve of water. The water
19	was used to irrigate dry farmland. It was also used as a
31	water supply by nearby cities and towns.
38	But the biggest benefit of Hoover Dam is its
47	hydroelectric power. The Hoover Dam makes a huge
55	amount of electricity. Every year it brings power to
64	1.3 million people in California, Nevada, and Arizona.
71	As an energy source, the Hoover Dam is clean and
81	cheap to run. It does not pollute the air the way fossil **fuels**
94	would. However, this huge dam has had some bad effects
104	on the environment. The landscape of the area will never
114	be the same. The river can no longer carry rich soil to the
127	lands it flooded. Fish and other wildlife have lost their homes.
138	But the Hoover Dam is here to stay. It is a modern
150	wonder of the United States. 155

Comprehension Check

1. How do you know that the author's purpose is to persuade the reader that the Hoover Dam is helpful? **Author's Purpose**

2. Compare the effects of fossil fuels with the effects of the dam. **Compare and Contrast**

	Words Read	–	Number of Errors	=	Words Correct Score
First Read		–		=	
Second Read		–		=	

© Macmillan/McGraw-Hill

TEKS 4.1 Read aloud grade-level stories with fluency and comprehension.

Ima and the Great Texas Ostrich
Race • **Grade 4/Unit 4** 167

Name _____

Encyclopedias and other reference books have **text features** to help readers locate information. **Guide words** appear at the top of each page in an encyclopedia. The word on the left page is the first entry on that page. The word on the right page is the last entry on that page. In the encyclopedia entry, **headings** are in boldfaced print. Headings tell you what different parts of the entry are about. Entries usually end with **cross-references** that tell you where else to look in the encyclopedia for more information on the subject. A cross-reference usually begins with the words *See also*.

Like most expository text, an encyclopedia entry contains a **topic sentence**. The topic sentence tells you what the entry is going to be about. Each entry also has a **concluding sentence**. This sentence often provides a final detail about the entry topic.

Look at the encyclopedia entries on pages 498–501 in your book. Then complete the items.

1. What guide word is at the top of page 499? _____

2. Use the headings to tell about the entry on page 499. _____

_____

3. What fact do you learn about Jane Addams from the caption in that entry?

_____

4. What cross-reference is listed at the end of the entry for Ima Hogg?

_____

5. What fact do you learn about Ima Hogg in the concluding sentence of

the entry? _____

_____

TEKS **4.11 (D)** Use multiple text features to gain an overview of text and to locate information.

Name _____

An encyclopedia has **multiple text features** that help readers find information. Articles are in alphabetical order. **Guide words** are usually found at the top. They show the first and last article on the page. The boldfaced article **title** tells what or whom the article is about. **Headings** divide the article into sections and tell what each section is about.

Use the following encyclopedia page to answer the questions.

Ferguson / festival

Ferguson, Miriam Amanda
(1875–1961)

Miriam Ferguson was born in Texas in 1875. She received a college education. In 1899, she married James Edward Ferguson.

First Lady of Texas James Ferguson was elected governor of Texas in 1915. He was re-elected and impeached during his second term. During this time, Miriam became known as "Ma." This was a combination of her first two initials.

~~fermentation~~

It also reflected her devotion to her husband and daughters.

Governor of Texas James Ferguson was not allowed to run for governor again. In 1924, "Ma" entered the race. She promised voters that her husband would advise her on polices. She won the election, becoming the first female governor of Texas and the second female governor in the United States.

1. Look at the guide words. What is the first article on this page about?

_____

2. Under what heading would you learn that James Ferguson was

impeached during his second term? _____

3. Use the headings to help you find the following information: In what year

did Miriam Ferguson become governor of Texas?_____

TEKS **4.11 (D)** Use multiple text features to gain an overview of the contents of text and to locate information.

Name _____

Analogies compare two pairs of words, often using **synonyms** or **antonyms**. For example, "happy is to joyful as significance is to importance" is an analogy using synonyms. "Up is to down as conserve is to waste" is an analogy using antonyms.

A. Choose the best word to complete the analogy. Write the correct letter on the line.

1. open is to closed as wild is to _____

   a. savage   **b.** quiet   **c.** tame   **d.** barbaric

2. advance is to retreat as comedy is to _____

   a. tragedy   **b.** music   **c.** jokes   **d.** laughter

3. close is to shut as perform is to _____

   a. forget   **b.** act   **c.** imitate   **d.** quiet

4. agree is to disagree as feast is to _____

   a. Thanksgiving   **b.** hunger   **c.** festival   **d.** famine

5. child is to kid as drama is to _____

   a. play   **b.** tragic   **c.** violence   **d.** comic

6. jumped is to leaped as laughed is to _____

   a. cried   **b.** hoped   **c.** chuckled   **d.** smiled

B. On each line below, write an analogy using synonyms and an analogy using antonyms.

7. _____

8. _____

© Macmillan/McGraw-Hill

TEKS   **4.2 (C)** Complete analogies using knowledge of antonyms and synonyms.

A. Reading Strategy: Make Inferences

Making inferences will help you understand what you read. Keep in mind that you should support every inference with details from the text. Choose a text that you are reading this week, and complete the chart.

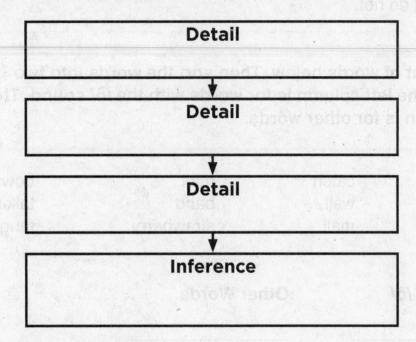

Detail

↓

Detail

↓

Detail

↓

Inference

B. Independent Reading Log

Choose something you would like to read. After reading, complete the reading log. Be sure to paraphrase, or tell the main idea or meaning of the text. Keep the details or events in the correct order. You may use the log to talk to others about what you read.

Genre _____

Title _____

Author _____

This Text Is About _____

_____

_____

TEKS **4.9** Read independently for a sustained period of time and paraphrase what the reading was about, maintaining meaning and logical order.
RC-4 (D) Make inferences about text and use textual evidence to support understanding.

Ima and the Great Texas Ostrich Race • Grade 4/Unit 4   **171**

Name _____

The underlined letters in the following words show you
different ways to spell the /ô/ sound: **bald**, **stalk**, **straw**,
caught. Notice that in **bald** you pronounce the **l**, but that in
stalk you do not.

**Read the list of words below. Then sort the words into two
columns. The left column is for words with the /ô/ sound. The
right column is for other words.**

laws	catch	malt	bows
sale	wall	band	talking
wail	mall	strawberry	taught

Words with /ô/   **Other Words**

_____   _____

_____   _____

_____   _____

_____   _____

_____   _____

_____   _____

_____   _____

TEKS 3.1 (E) Monitor accuracy in decoding.

Name _____

assembled   assured   headlines
unstable   applauded   hoisting

Write the word that matches each meaning. Then write your answer in the crossword puzzle.

Across

1. built _____

2. certain _____

4. not steady _____

Down

1. clapped to show appreciation for a performance _____

3. newspaper article titles _____

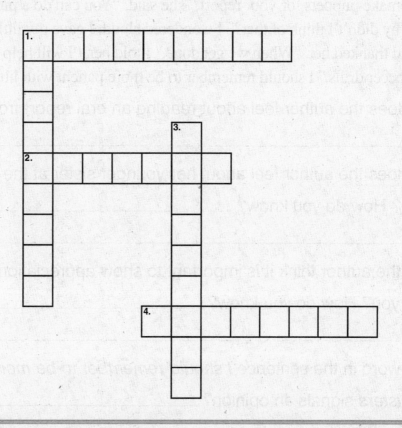

TEKS 4.2 (B) Use the context of the sentence to determine the meaning of unfamiliar words.

My Brothers' Flying Machine   **173**
Grade 4/Unit 4

An **author's perspective** is his or her point of view. It may include the author's attitudes and opinions about a subject. The words *best*, *worst*, *should*, and *ought to* are often used to signal the author's opinion.

Read the autobiographical essay. Then answer the questions.

I was having the worst day. My oral report was due tomorrow and I still couldn't think of how to make it interesting. I didn't want to bore everyone by just reading from note cards. Just then, my little sister Nita came bursting in. "Great!" I thought. "Just what I need—a visit from Nita the Nuisance."

"What's wrong?" Nita asked.

"My report is due tomorrow and I can't think of how to make it more exciting," I explained.

Nita thought for a moment. Then her face lit up. "I'll be right back, Gina," she exclaimed. When she returned, she had a paper bag on each hand. "Let's make puppets for your report," she said. "You can do a puppet show."

"Why didn't I think of that?" I wondered aloud. I gave my little sister a hug and thanked her. "When we get done," I told her, "I will help you practice your soccer drills." I should remember to be more patient with little sisters!

1. How does the author feel about reading an oral report from note cards?

   _____

2. How does the author feel about her younger sister at the beginning of the essay? How do you know? _____

   _____

3. Does the author think it is important to show appreciation when someone helps you? How do you know? _____

   _____

4. What word in the sentence *I should remember to be more patient with little sisters* signals an opinion? _____

TEKS 5.7 Identify the literary language used in autobiographies, including how authors present major events in a person's life.

Name _____

As you read *My Brothers' Flying Machine*, fill in the Author's Perspective Map.

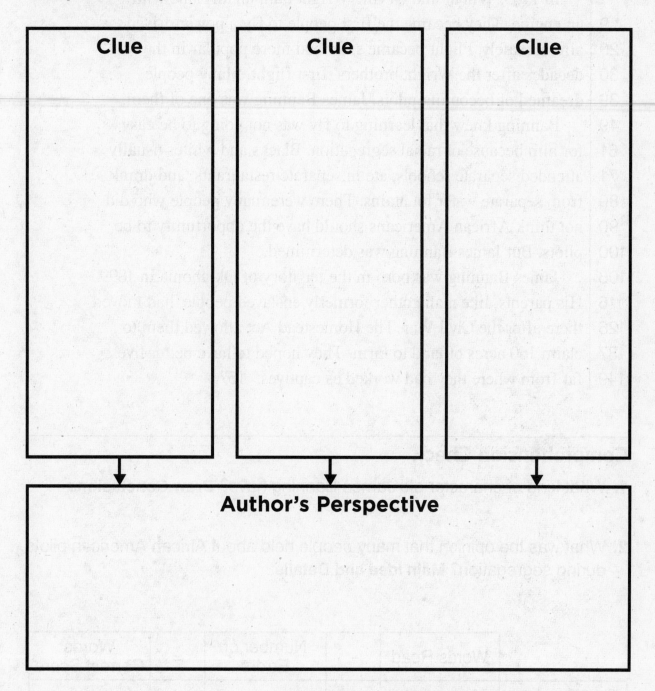

Clue	Clue	Clue

Author's Perspective

How does the information you wrote in your Author's Perspective Map help you understand *My Brothers' Flying Machine*?

TEKS 5.7 Identify the literary language used in biographies, including how authors present major events in a person's life.

My Brothers' Flying Machine
Grade 4/Unit 4   175

As I read, I will pay attention to my reading rate.

	In 1903, Wilbur and Orville Wright built an airplane with
9	an engine. They became the first people to fly a power-driven
20	aircraft safely. Flight became safer and more popular in the
30	decades after the Wright brothers' first flight. Many people
39	dreamed of becoming pilots. James Banning was one of them.
49	Banning knew that learning to fly was not going to be easy
61	for him because of racial segregation. Blacks and whites usually
71	attended separate schools, ate in separate restaurants, and drank
80	from separate water fountains. There were many people who did
90	not think African Americans should have the opportunity to be
100	pilots. But James Banning was determined.
106	James Banning was born in the territory of Oklahoma in 1899.
116	His parents, like many other formerly enslaved people, had moved
126	there after the Civil War. The Homestead Act allowed them to
137	claim 160 acres of land to farm. They hoped to have better lives
149	far from where they had worked as captives. 157

Comprehension Check

1. What kind of character did James Banning have? **Draw Conclusions**

2. What was the opinion that many people held about African American pilots during segregation? **Main Idea and Details**

	Words Read	–	Number of Errors	=	Words Correct Score
First Read		–		=	
Second Read		–		=	

© Macmillan/McGraw-Hill

TEKS 4.1 Read aloud grade-level stories with fluency and comprehension.

Name _____

> A **fact** is a statement that can be proved true. You can **verify**, or check, facts by using sources such as encyclopedias, atlases, biographies, textbooks, reliable Web sites, and other references. An **opinion** is a statement that tells a person's feelings or beliefs. Unlike facts, opinions cannot be proved true.

Read the passage. Then answer the questions.

There are many different types of flowers. Roses are a type of flower that grows on bushes and can have thorns. Roses come in several colors such as red, white, pink, and yellow. Red roses are the prettiest. People often give roses as a gift. Roses are the best gift to give on Valentine's Day.

1. Write one opinion from the passage. _____

_____

2. Write one fact from the passage. _____

_____

_____

3. What sources could you use to check this fact? _____

_____

4. Write another fact from the passage. _____

_____

_____

5. How could you check that this is a fact? _____

_____

_____

TEKS **4.11 (B)** Distinguish fact from opinion in a text and explain how to verify what is a fact.

> A **narrative poem** tells a story about a fictional or real event.
> **Repetition** occurs when a word or phrase is repeated throughout
> a poem. **Personification** is when human characteristics are
> given to an animal, a thing, or an idea.

Read the poem. Then answer the questions that follow.

Operation Migration

A new millennium approaches, filled with hope and cheer.
But will it see the whooping crane for many of its years?
A forgotten resolution to migrate and survive
Keeps the birds from knowing the route or how or why.

A pilot has a brainstorm, filled with hope and cheer.
But will it teach the whooping crane to live for many years?
A pilot and a glider would lead the way and show
The whooping cranes that followed where the route is, so they'd know.

The pilot glances back and he's filled with hope and cheer.
Two rows of flapping whooping cranes follow in the rear.
Suspended in the balance between the Earth and sky,
Will the birds remember? Will the birds survive?

Another nest of hatchlings, filled with hope and cheer.
Another brood of whooping cranes to follow late this year.
A pilot in a glider between the Earth and sky.
Each year more birds remember and the whooping crane survives.

1. Which phrases in the poem are examples of repetition?

_____

_____

2. What is one example of personification in the poem?

_____

_____

_____

© Macmillan/McGraw-Hill

TEKS 4.4 Explain how the structural elements of poetry relate to form.

A **suffix** is a word part that can be added to the end of a word. Suffixes may come from Latin, Greek, and other languages. A number of suffixes mean "one who." When added to the end of a verb, these suffixes change a verb into a noun. The Latin suffixes -*er* and -*or*, the Greek suffix -*ist*, and the French suffix -*ant* all mean "one who" when added to the end of a verb.

teach + *er* = *teacher* (a person who teaches)
act + *or* = *actor* (a person who acts)
copy + *ist* = *copyist* (one who copies)
serv + *ant* = *servant* (one who serves)

Look for the verb. Then, add the correct suffix to make a word that means the same as the entire phrase in bold.

1. **A person who travels** in an airplane is a _____.

2. **A person who invents** a new machine is an _____.

3. **A person who immigrates** is an _____.

4. **A person who makes** a kite is a kite _____.

5. **A person who bicycles** is a _____.

6. **A person who survives** a crash is a _____.

7. **A person who explores** a new idea is an _____.

8. **A person who gets a degree in biology** is a

_____.

TEKS 4.2 (A) Determine the meaning of grade-level academic English words derived from Latin, Greek, or other linguistic affixes.

Name _____

A. Reading Strategy: Make Inferences

Making inferences will help you understand what you read. Keep in mind that you should support every inference with details from the text. Choose a text that you are reading this week, and complete the activity.

Before Reading Note the kinds of inferences that you might make while reading the text.

I will read	I might make inferences about
Fiction/Drama	characters' actions, events, the author's message
Poetry	the speaker's meaning, the author's message
Biography/Autobiography	the subject's actions, events, the author's message
Informational Text	causes and effects, problems and solution
Persuasive Text	the author's message, ideas used to support the author's message

During Reading Use ideas from the chart and clues from the text to make inferences.

After Reading Explain how you used an idea from the chart and clues from the text to help you make an inference.

B. Independent Reading Log

Choose something you would like to read. After reading, complete the reading log. Be sure to paraphrase, or tell the main idea or meaning of the text. Keep the details or events in the correct order. You may use the log to talk to others about what you read.

Genre _____

Title _____

Author _____

This Text Is About _____

_____

© Macmillan/McGraw-Hill

TEKS **4.9** Read independently for a sustained period of time and paraphrase what the reading was about, maintaining meaning and logical order. **RC-4 (D)** Make inferences about text and use textual evidence to support understanding.

Name _____

A two-syllable word with the **VCCV pattern** is usually divided between the two consonants.

swal low   wel come

The first syllable of a VCCV word is a **closed syllable**. That means it has a short vowel sound and ends in a consonant. The second syllable may also be closed.

Divide each word below into syllables. Write the syllables in the blanks provided.

1. copper _____ _____

2. member _____ _____

3. planner _____ _____

4. market _____ _____

5. summer _____ _____

6. slender _____ _____

7. fossil _____ _____

8. blanket _____ _____

9. fiction _____ _____

10. witness _____ _____

Name _____

| climate | silken | lumbering |
| lurk | shimmer | eerie |

A. Substitute a vocabulary word for the underlined word or words in each sentence.

1. The rattlesnake's rattle makes a <u>scary</u> sound, warning us to keep out of

its way. _____

2. Alligators often <u>lie in wait</u> in the reeds until small animals come near.

_____

3. A bear's <u>heavy, awkward</u> step warns small creatures in its path.

_____

4. The surfaces of frozen ponds <u>glow brightly</u> in the winter sunlight.

_____

5. Cacti are plants adapted to the <u>usual weather</u> in the desert.

_____

6. A spider's web is made of <u>soft, smooth</u> strands. _____

B. Choose three vocabulary words and use them in one sentence.

_____

_____

_____

TEKS **4.2 (B)** Use the context of the sentence to determine the meaning of unfamiliar words.

Name _____

The **main idea** of a selection tells you what it is mostly about. The supporting **details** in the selection help you to understand the main idea. To find the main idea, think about what the supporting details have in common.

Read the passage and answer the questions that follow.

Many newborn rattlesnakes do not survive their first year of life. A baby rattlesnake is only about ten inches long. Although they have short fangs and a poisonous bite, they are often eaten by birds and animals. The adult rattlesnakes do not raise their young. The young snakes are entirely on their own. Many die of hunger. In the winter, they die if they do not find a warm place where they can hibernate.

1. What supporting details tell you how young rattlesnakes are in danger? List two details on the lines below.

_____

_____

_____

2. What supporting detail tells you how baby rattlesnakes can survive in the winter?

_____

3. What supporting detail tells you how baby rattlesnakes can attempt to defend themselves?

_____

4. What is the main idea of this passage?

_____

TEKS 4.11 (A) Summarize the main idea and supporting details in text in ways that maintain meaning.

A Walk in the Desert
Grade 4/Unit 5
183

Name _____

As you read _A Walk in the Desert_, fill in the Main Idea Chart.

Detail
Detail
Main Idea

Detail
Detail
Detail
Main Idea

How does the information you wrote in the Main Idea Chart help you
to summarize _A Walk in the Desert_?

TEKS 4.11 (A) Summarize the main idea and supporting details in text in ways
that maintain meaning.

Name _____

As I read, I will pay attention to my reading rate.

	The Sahara is the world's largest desert. It is nearly
10	the size of the United States. The Sahara extends over
20	10 countries in northern Africa. Like all deserts, it gets
29	fewer than 10 inches (24 cm) of rain a year.
37	In parts of the Sahara, you can see nothing but sand for
49	miles. A sand dune forms when wind carries sand over a
60	large rock. The sand drops, and gradually a hill of sand
71	grows.
72	However, about 80 percent of the world's deserts are
80	not sandy. This is true within the Sahara as well. Deserts
91	begin as rock. The rock is worn away and broken apart by
103	wind, rainstorms, and changing temperatures. Over time,
110	the rock is broken into smaller and smaller pieces. The
120	rock breaks down first into boulders, then into stones, and
130	finally into sand. In some places, the Sahara is made up of
142	huge rocks and gravel. 146

Comprehension Check

1. What makes the Sahara a desert? **Main Idea and Details**

2. State the details of how a desert is formed. **Main Idea and Details**

	Words Read	–	Number of Errors	=	Words Correct Score
First Read		–		=	
Second Read		–		=	

© Macmillan/McGraw-Hill

TEKS 4.1 Read aloud grade-level stories with fluency and comprehension.

A Walk in the Desert
Grade 4/Unit 5
185

Name _____

Sometimes an author's purpose for writing is directly **stated**, but often it is not. Instead, the author's purpose is **implied**, and readers must use clues from the text to figure out the author's purpose. The first clue is whether the selection is fiction or nonfiction. Authors usually write fiction to entertain. They write nonfiction to inform, persuade, or explain.

1. Reread *Food Chains: Predator vs. Prey*, and fill in the Author's Purpose Chart.

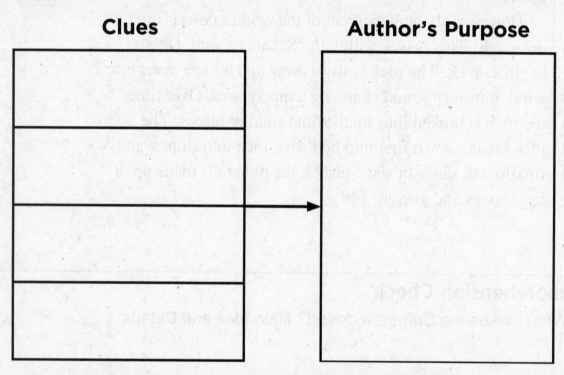

Clues

Author's Purpose

2. Is the author's purpose in *Food Chains: Predator vs. Prey* a stated or an implied purpose? Explain how you know.

_____

_____

_____

TEKS 4.10 Explain the difference between a stated and an implied purpose for an expository text.

Name _____

A flow chart is a good way to show a **process** from start to finish.
It uses words joined by arrows to show the order of steps.

Look at the flow chart below. Then answer the questions.

The Water Cycle

EVAPORATION
The sun heats the water in oceans, lakes, or rivers and turns it into steam. Then, the steam, or vapor, rises in the air.

CONDENSATION
The vapor in the air cools and changes to liquid. That liquid is held in the clouds.

COLLECTION
Water that falls back to earth can be soaked up into the ground, or it can run back into the oceans, lakes, or rivers.

PRECIPITATION
When enough water collects in the clouds, the clouds can't hold it. The water can fall as rain, snow, or hail.

1. What natural process does this flow chart show?

_____

2. What happens after collection?

_____

3. What happens during condensation?

_____

4. What two things can happen to water during collection?

_____

Practice

Name _____

Vocabulary Strategy:
Context Clues:
Surrounding Words

Sometimes **surrounding words** can provide the context you need to figure out the meaning of an unfamiliar word. Context clues may include examples and definitions.

Read the following sentences. Circle the answer that best fits in the blank.

1. A **border** _____ often separates one country from another.

    a. of green flowers   **b.** such as a river

2. **Venomous** snakes, _____, kill prey with their poisonous bite.

    a. including rattlesnakes   **b.** in the zoo

3. In the West, the open **range** of _____ gradually became fenced in.

    a. empty land   **b.** deep lakes

4. Many desert animals hide from **predators**, _____.

    a. like cows   **b.** or animals that hunt them

5. At high **elevations** _____ there are fewer trees and plants.

    a. under the ocean   **b.** near the top of mountains

6. **Fledglings**, _____, hatch from eggs in the spring.

    a. such as baby wrens   **b.** such as full-grown hawks

7. **Nocturnal** animals, _____, look for food between dusk and dawn.

    a. like bats and owls   **b.** like whales and dolphins

8. Western farmers plant **orchards** full of _____.

    a. orange and lemon trees   **b.** chickens

© Macmillan/McGraw-Hill

TEKS **4.2 (B)** Use the context of the sentence to determine the meaning of unfamiliar words.

Name _____

A. Reading Strategy: Summarize

Summarizing information and ideas from texts will help you understand what you read. Keep the meaning of the text clear. Include information from the text in an order that makes sense. Choose a text that you are reading this week, and complete the activity.

Record important events or ideas from the text.

_____

_____

_____

Use your notes to summarize the text.

_____

_____

_____

B. Independent Reading Log

Choose something that you would like to read. After reading, complete the reading log. Be sure to paraphrase, or tell the main idea or meaning of the text. Keep the details or events in the proper order. You may use your log to talk to others about what you read.

Genre _____

Title _____

Author _____

This Text Is About _____

_____

TEKS 4.9 Read independently for a sustained period of time and paraphrase what the reading was about, maintaining meaning and logical order. **RC-4 (E)** Summarize information in text, maintaining meaning and logical order.

A Walk in the Desert 189
Grade 4/Unit 5

Name _____

An **open syllable** ends with a long vowel sound. Open first syllables have the **V/CV pattern**.

A **closed syllable** ends with a consonant. The vowel sound is short. Closed first syllables may have the **VC/V pattern**.

Read the words below. Listen for the vowel sound in the first syllable and draw a slash to show where to divide each word. If you have doubts, look up the word in a dictionary. Then, on the line, write whether the first syllable is open or closed.

1. h a b i t _____

2. n e v e r _____

3. w i p e r _____

4. t a l e n t _____

5. r o b i n _____

6. m e t e r _____

7. c i d e r _____

8. l e v e l _____

9. p r o m i s e _____

10. f a m o u s _____

11. l i m i t _____

12. f i n i s h _____

TEKS 3.1 (E) Monitor accuracy in decoding.

Name _____

| interfere | guardian | awkward |
| agile | proclaimed | convinced |

Use the context clues in each sentence to help you decide which vocabulary word fits best in the blank.

Small Snake couldn't move as easily as the other snakes. "I'm so

_____," he cried.

Caterpillar offered to lend Small Snake a few legs. The young reptile

stumbled on them.

Raven stuck out her chest and proudly _____, "I am the

one who can make this poor snake _____ enough to slither

here and there."

Mr. Caterpillar offered to help, but Raven waved him away and said,

"Do not _____ with what I am doing." She was

_____ her way was best.

She made a straight line of poles in the ground. "Now,
go in and out from each pole to the next."

Small Snake found that he was curving and slithering.
"I know how to do it now!" he cried.

Raven said, "Caterpillar, you will watch out for

Small Snake and be his _____ until he
grows up."

© Macmillan/McGraw-Hill

TEKS **4.2 (B)** Use the context of the sentence to determine the meaning of
unfamiliar words.

Name _____

> A story usually begins by introducing a character and the **problem** he or she has. The steps the character takes to solve the problem are the events of a story. A story ends with the **solution** to the problem. The problem, events, and solution make up the plot of a story.

Read the passage below. Then answer the questions.

A box came in the mail for Denisha, but it had no return address. When Denisha opened the box, she found a blue jacket and matching pants. She tried on the pants and jacket. They fit perfectly, and blue was Denisha's favorite color. She wanted to thank the sender. She asked her mother and sister if they had mailed the package, but they both said no. Denisha looked again at the outside of the box, and then she smiled. "I figured it out! The stamp says that the box was mailed from Detroit. Grandma lives there. She must have sent it."

1. Who is the main character? _____

2. What is the problem? _____

_____

3. What is the first thing Denisha does to solve her problem? _____

_____

4. How does Denisha solve her problem? _____

_____

5. What might happen next? _____

_____

TEKS 4.6 (A) Sequence and summarize the plot's main events and explain their influence on future events.

As you read *Roadrunner's Dance*, fill in the Problem and Solution Chart.

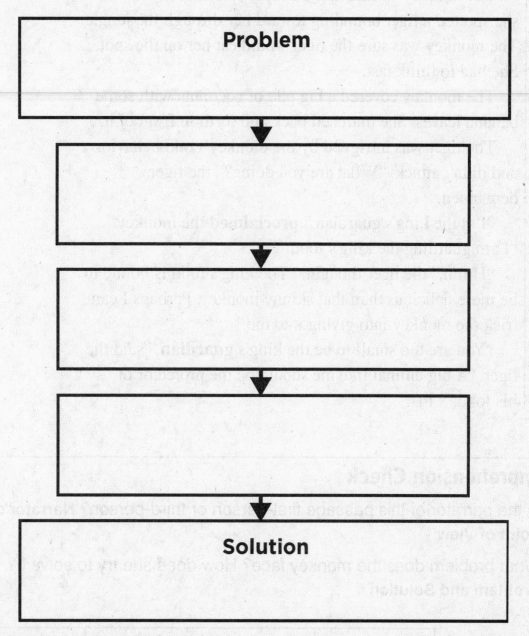

Problem

Solution

How does the information you wrote in the Problem and Solution Chart help you summarize *Roadrunner's Dance*?

Name _____

As I read, I will pay attention to intonation and phrasing.

	The monkey was having a simply splendid day. Then
9	she spotted a tiger bounding toward her through the jungle.
19	The monkey was sure the tiger would eat her on the spot.
31	She had to think fast.
36	The monkey covered a big pile of coconuts with some
46	banana leaves. She marched back and forth in front of it.
57	The tiger was intrigued by the monkey's odd behavior
66	and didn't attack. "What are you doing?" the tiger
75	demanded.
76	"I'm the king's guardian," **proclaimed** the monkey.
83	"I am guarding the king's food."
89	"Hmm," the tiger thought. "The king's food is bound to
99	be more delicious than that skinny monkey. Perhaps I can
109	trick the monkey into giving it to me."
117	"You are too small to be the king's **guardian**," said the
128	tiger. "A big animal like me should be the protector of
139	his food." 141

Comprehension Check

1. Is the narrator of this passage first-person or third-person? **Narrator's Point of View**

2. What problem does the monkey face? How does she try to solve it? **Problem and Solution**

	Words Read	–	Number of Errors	=	Words Correct Score
First Read		–		=	
Second Read		–		=	

© Macmillan/McGraw-Hill

TEKS 4.1 Read aloud grade-level stories with fluency and comprehension.

Authors use **sensory language** to create **imagery**, or pictures in the reader's mind. Sensory language helps readers see, hear, smell, taste, or feel something. Metaphors and similes are types of sensory language. A **metaphor** is a figure of speech in which two very different objects or ideas are said to be alike. **Similes** also compare two different things, usually by using the words *like* or *as*.

Read the poem. Then answer the questions.

Outside my bedroom window, a storm rages.
The wind is like a lone wolf howling.
The tree is a giant, waving his arms.
The lightning is a brilliant fireworks display.
The thunder is as loud as a drumbeat.
I am a butterfly in a cocoon, safe from the storm.

1. What is this poem about? _____

2. Circle two similes that appear in the poem.

3. What two things are being compared in each simile?

_____

_____

4. Underline two metaphors that appear in the poem.

5. What two things are said to be alike in each metaphor?

_____

_____

TEKS 4.8 Identify the author's use of similes and metaphors to produce imagery.

Roadrunner's Dance
Grade 4/Unit 5
195

Foreshadowing is the use of clues to hint at what is going to happen in a story. Authors use foreshadowing to build suspense. Dark clouds often foreshadow a storm.

Symbolism is the use of an object or action to represent an idea, such as love, pride, or strength. A dove is often a symbol for peace.

A. Read the passage. Then answer the questions.

Mouse and Bird were strolling through the desert. As always, Mouse was paying close attention to his surroundings. Bird was busy whistling. "We're walking past Tarantula's house," Mouse said. "Keep your eyes open!" Bird just kept whistling instead of paying attention. Mouse was safely past the rock when he looked behind him. He saw eight hairy legs stealthily creeping toward Bird.

1. What does Mouse's warning foreshadow? _____

_____

_____

2. What detail about Bird's actions foreshadows that he might be in danger?

_____

_____

B. Read the question. Write your answers on the lines.

3. Which season is usually a symbol of new beginnings? Why? _____

_____

_____

© Macmillan/McGraw-Hill

TEKS 5.8 (A) Evaluate the impact of sensory details, imagery, and figurative language in literary text.

Name _____

A **synonym** is a word that means the same or almost the same as another word. For example, a synonym for *guardian* is *protector*. You can use a thesaurus to find synonyms.

A. Replace each word in parentheses with one of these synonyms.

| clumsy | nimble | announced | meddle | certain |

1. "Don't (interfere) _____ with my plans to be king of the road!"

2. The roadrunner was (awkward) _____ when he first tried to run and jump.

3. He was (convinced) _____ he could not learn.

4. Later, when Roadrunner danced in circles, you could see how (agile)

   _____ he had become.

5. "Roadrunner is our hero!" the animals (proclaimed) _____.

B. Write a sentence using a synonym for each of the words in bold type.

6. **frightened** and **trembled** _____

   _____

7. **yelled** and **bragged** _____

   _____

8. **hopped** and **quick** _____

   _____

Name _____

A. Reading Strategy: Summarize

Summarizing information and ideas from texts will help you understand what you read. Keep the meaning of the text clear. Include information from the text in an order that makes sense. Choose a text that you are reading this week, and complete the items.

Record important events or ideas from the text.

_____

_____

_____

Use your notes to summarize the text.

_____

_____

_____

B. Reading Strategy: Listening and Speaking

Choose something you would like to read. After reading, create a brief summary of the selection and present your summary to a partner. Be sure to state the main ideas or events clearly, maintaining meaning and logical order. Answer any questions from your partner with appropriate detail.

Then listen attentively as your partner presents his or her summary. Ask relevant questions and make pertinent comments.

© Macmillan/McGraw-Hill

TEKS **4.9** Read independently for a sustained period of time and paraphrase what the reading was about, maintaining meaning and logical order.
RC-4 (E) Summarize information in text, maintaining meaning and logical order.

Name _____

Sometimes two letters together stand for one vowel sound. This is called a **vowel team**. When two vowels team up in a word, they stay in the same syllable.

oat/m**ea**l   r**ai**l/r**oa**d

Underline the vowel team in each word. Then write another word that has the same vowel team.

1. mailbox _____

2. seashore _____

3. mouthwash _____

4. steely _____

5. boastful _____

6. dreamlike _____

7. staircase _____

8. toaster _____

9. unclear _____

10. sooner _____

A. Read the vocabulary words. Use the clues to complete the puzzle.

| roamed | completed | journey | natural | relocated |

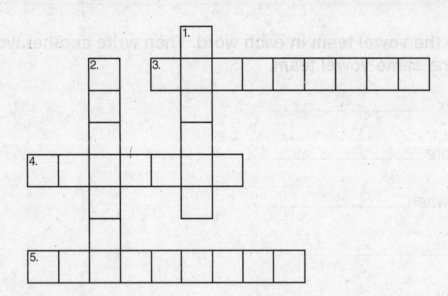

Across

3. finished
4. trip
5. moved

Down

1. wandered
2. not artificial

B. Write a sentence using two of the words.

6. _____

_____

TEKS **4.2 (B)** Use the context of the sentence to determine the meaning of unfamiliar words.

© Macmillan/McGraw-Hill

Name _____

The **main idea** of a selection tells you what it is mostly about.
The supporting **details** help you understand the main idea. To
find the main idea, think about how the details are connected.

**Read the paragraph below. Then identify three details and the
main idea.**

Cumberland Gap National Park is under attack! A plant called kudzu
threatens the park's ecosystem. Few animals eat kudzu, and it grows so fast
it's been called "the vine that ate the South." It can grow a foot a night! It
grows even after it has been dosed with herbicide, or plant killer. That's
bad news for native plants and trees. Kudzu grows right over them. It takes
the sunlight plants need to live. Bits of kudzu came to Cumberland stuck
to truck tires. The trucks were there to build a road. Now park rangers
cut kudzu back. They apply herbicide to the plant's huge root. They could
bring in goats because goats eat kudzu. But goats also eat native plants.
Solving the kudzu problem will be tricky.

1. Supporting detail:

_____

2. Supporting detail:

_____

3. Supporting detail:

_____

4. Main idea:

_____

_____

TEKS 4.11 (A) Summarize the main idea and supporting details in text in ways
that maintain meaning.

Animals Come Home to Our
National Parks • Grade 4/Unit 5 **201**

Name _____

As you read *Animals Come Home to Our National Parks*,
fill in the Main Idea Chart.

Detail
Detail
Detail
Main Idea

How does the information you wrote in the Main Idea Chart help you
summarize *Animals Come Home to Our National Parks*?

202 Animals Come Home to Our
National Parks • **Grade 4/Unit 5**

TEKS **4.11 (A)** Summarize the main idea and supporting details in text in ways
that maintain meaning.

As you read *Animals Come Home to Our National Parks*, fill in the Main Idea Chart.

| Detail |
| Detail |
| Detail |
| Main Idea |

How does the information you wrote in the Main Idea Chart help you summarize *Animals Come Home to Our National Parks*?

TEKS **4.11 (A)** Summarize the main idea and supporting details in text in ways that maintain meaning.

Sometimes two letters together stand for one vowel sound. This is called a **vowel team**. When two vowels team up in a word, they stay in the same syllable.
oat/meal   **rai**l/r**oa**d

Underline the vowel team in each word. Then write another word that has the same vowel team.

1. mailbox _____

2. seashore _____

3. mouthwash _____

4. steely _____

5. boastful _____

6. dreamlike _____

7. staircase _____

8. toaster _____

9. unclear _____

10. sooner _____

TEKS **3.1 (E)** Monitor accuracy in decoding.

© Macmillan/McGraw-Hill

A. Read the vocabulary words. Use the clues to complete the puzzle.

| roamed | completed | journey | natural | relocated |

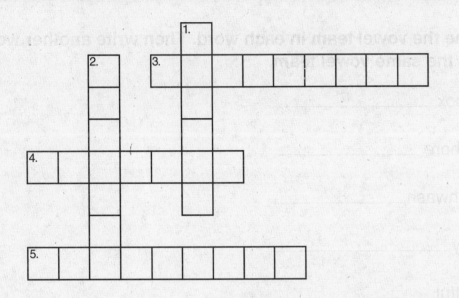

Across

3. finished
4. trip
5. moved

Down

1. wandered
2. not artificial

B. Write a sentence using two of the words.

6. _____

The **main idea** of a selection tells you what it is mostly about. The supporting **details** help you understand the main idea. To find the main idea, think about how the details are connected.

Read the paragraph below. Then identify three details and the main idea.

Cumberland Gap National Park is under attack! A plant called kudzu threatens the park's ecosystem. Few animals eat kudzu, and it grows so fast it's been called "the vine that ate the South." It can grow a foot a night! It grows even after it has been dosed with herbicide, or plant killer. That's bad news for native plants and trees. Kudzu grows right over them. It takes the sunlight plants need to live. Bits of kudzu came to Cumberland stuck to truck tires. The trucks were there to build a road. Now park rangers cut kudzu back. They apply herbicide to the plant's huge root. They could bring in goats because goats eat kudzu. But goats also eat native plants. Solving the kudzu problem will be tricky.

1. Supporting detail:

_____

2. Supporting detail:

_____

3. Supporting detail:

_____

4. Main idea:

_____

_____

TEKS **4.11 (A)** Summarize the main idea and supporting details in text in ways that maintain meaning.

Animals Come Home to Our
National Parks • Grade 4/Unit 5 201

Name _____

As I read, I will pay attention to the pronunciation of vocabulary words and other hard words.

	Acadia National Park has dark green mountains. When
8	you look down from these mountains you see the icy
18	Atlantic Ocean. You see ocean waves crashing against
26	rocky shores. These 48,000 acres (194 sq km) of **natural**
34	beauty have a long history. It is a history full of stories
46	about people who loved this land of mountain and sea.
56	These people worked to make sure that everyone could
65	enjoy it.
67	Acadia National Park is spread out over a group of
77	islands off the coast of Maine. Most of the park is on
89	Mount Desert Island. The park has beautiful freshwater
97	lakes and ponds. There are trails for hiking in the
107	mountains or walking by the shore.
113	As you read, you will learn about the history of
123	this park. 125

Comprehension Check

1. Think about the details in the first paragraph. What is the main idea of the paragraph? **Main Idea and Details**

2. What details would you use to describe the natural beauty of the park? Use sensory language. **Sensory Language**

	Words Read	–	Number of Errors	=	Words Correct Score
First Read		–		=	
Second Read		–		=	

TEKS 4.1 Read aloud grade-level stories with fluency and comprehension.

A **cause** is the reason that something happens. An **effect** is something that happens as a result of a cause. Authors often show **explicit** cause-and-effect relationships by using signal words and phrases such as *because*, *due to*, and *as a result*. These signal words and phrases directly state the relationship between two events. When authors do not use signal words, the relationship is **implicit**, or implied. You must infer how the events are related.

Read the passage. Then complete the items.

Millions of people visit national parks each year. Some park officials worry that large numbers of visitors will cause damage to the parks. People who walk in the park trample plants and soil. As a result, the ground in some parks is beginning to erode, or wash away. As people drive through the parks, their cars put out harmful chemicals that may damage plant life. At one park, pine tree needles are turning yellow. Helicopters and airplanes that fly above the parks make loud noises. Park officials at another park believe that animals may be moving away from their homes and feeding grounds due to this noise.

1. Underline any signal words or phrases you find in the passage.

2. What implicit relationship can you infer from this passage?

_____

_____

3. Why is the ground washing away in some parks? _____

_____

4. What causes problems for animals at one park? _____

_____

_____

TEKS **4.11 (C)** Describe explicit and implicit relationships among ideas in texts organized by cause-and-effect.

A **dictionary** entry lists a word's meanings, its pronunciation and syllabication, part of speech, and examples of how to use the word.

Read the dictionary entry below. Then answer the questions that follow.

entry word

example of word in a sentence

lively 1. full of energy. The *lively* puppies romped around the room.
2. bright. The walls of Emma's room were painted a *lively* pink.

first meaning of word

second meaning of word

pronunciation

syllable division

other forms of the word

live·ly līv′lē *adjective,* **livelier, liveliest.**

part of speech

1. What is the entry word? _____

2. How many syllables does this word have? _____

3. To pronounce the word *lively*, is the vowel in the first syllable long or short? _____

4. What part of speech is *lively*? _____

5. Which definition best describes a fourth-grade class at recess?

_____

6. What other forms of *lively* are listed in the entry? _____

_____

TEKS 4.2 (E) Use a dictionary to determine the meanings, syllabication, and pronunciation of unknown words.

Animals Come Home to Our
National Parks • **Grade 4/Unit 5**   **205**

Name _____

Many English words are formed by adding word parts, such as prefixes and suffixes, to a basic word, or root word. Many words have roots that come from Latin, the language of ancient Rome.

- Words that have the **Latin root** *locat* have to do with places.
- Words that have the **Latin root** *duc* have to do with leading.

Complete each sentence with a word from the box that takes the place of the underlined words.

educate	relocate	location	conduct	deduce

1. When people build in places where animals live, animals are sometimes forced to move to a new place of activity or residence. _____

2. Many zoos and parks lead or guide tours to help people learn about the animals that live there. _____

3. Many experts can be led to a conclusion about what kinds of animals live in an area just by looking at animal tracks. _____

4. Some parks and zoos move to a different place animals whose habitats have been destroyed. _____

5. It is a good idea to lead yourself to learn about the animals that live in your community. _____

TEKS 4.2 (A) Determine the meaning of grade-level academic English words derived from Latin roots.

© Macmillan/McGraw-Hill

Name _____

The chronological order of events is the order in which things happen. Keeping track of the **sequence**, or order of events, helps you make sense of what is happening as you read.

Read the passage below. Then number the events that follow to show the correct sequence.

Miranda's parents were planning a trip to Mexico to go whale watching. Miranda's mother bought airline tickets on a travel Web site. Miranda's father asked his boss for time off. Miranda asked a neighbor to feed the family pets. Miranda's mother asked the post office to hold their mail.

On the day of the trip, the family drove to the airport. They stood in line and went through security. Finally they boarded the airplane and took off for Mexico.

1. Miranda's mother asked the post office to hold the mail. _____

2. They stood in line and went through security. _____

3. The family boarded the plane and took off for Mexico. _____

4. Miranda's parents were planning a trip to Mexico. _____

5. Miranda's father asked his boss for time off. _____

6. Miranda's mother bought airline tickets on a travel Web site. _____

7. Miranda asked a neighbor to feed the family pets. _____

8. On the day of the trip, the family drove to the airport. _____

TEKS 4.11 (C) Describe explicit relationships among ideas in texts organized by sequence.

Name _____

As you read *Adelina's Whales*, fill in the Sequence Chart.

```
┌─────────────────────────────┐
│                             │
│                             │
│                             │
└─────────────────────────────┘
              │
              ▼
┌─────────────────────────────┐
│                             │
│                             │
│                             │
└─────────────────────────────┘
              │
              ▼
┌─────────────────────────────┐
│                             │
│                             │
│                             │
└─────────────────────────────┘
```

How does the information you wrote in the Sequence Chart help you
to analyze the text structure of *Adelina's Whales*?

TEKS 4.11 (C) Describe explicit relationships among ideas in texts organized
by sequence.

220 Adelina's Whales • **Grade 4/Unit 5**

Name _____

As I read, I will pay attention to my reading rate and expression.

	Did you know that whales talk to each other? Whales
10	make sounds for different reasons. Some sounds are used to
20	locate calves. Others are used to find mates. Whales even use
31	sounds to warn other pod members that a predator is around.
42	Toothed whales click and whistle in order to locate food.
52	Baleen whales make knocking, moaning, snoring, and
59	rumbling noises. Humpback whales sing, but not during
67	feeding season. They save their tunes for the warmer waters
77	where they spend their breeding season. Some scientists
85	believe they are singing love songs. Other scientists think
94	they are sending out threats, like "Go away!" We may never
105	know exactly why whales sing.
110	Some humpback whales swim up to the surface and take
120	a few breaths. Then they dive under the water and start to
132	sing. They do not move when they sing. Their underwater
142	songs can be heard for miles. Sometimes they sing for a half
154	hour without stopping. 157

Comprehension Check

1. What does a humpback whale do before it sings? **Sequence**

2. Why might a whale need to communicate with another whale? **Draw Conclusions**

	Words Read	–	Number of Errors	=	Words Correct Score
First Read		–		=	
Second Read		–		=	

TEKS 4.1 Read aloud grade-level stories with fluency and comprehension.

Adelina's Whales • Grade 4/Unit 5 **221**

Name _____

Encyclopedias and other reference books use **text features** to help readers locate information. **Guide words** appear at the top of each page in an encyclopedia. The word on the left page is the first entry on that page. The word on the right page is the last entry on that page. Entries between the guide words are arranged in alphabetical order. Guide words help you locate entries quickly. Entries usually end with **cross-references** that tell you where to look in the encyclopedia for more information on the subject. A cross-reference usually begins with the words *See also*.

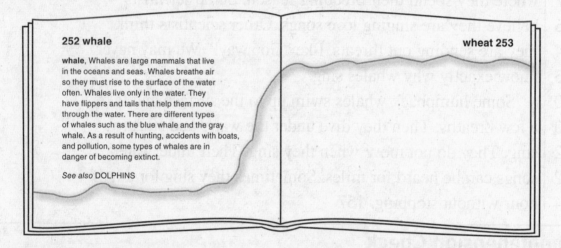

252 whale

whale, Whales are large mammals that live in the oceans and seas. Whales breathe air so they must rise to the surface of the water often. Whales live only in the water. They have flippers and tails that help them move through the water. There are different types of whales such as the blue whale and the gray whale. As a result of hunting, accidents with boats, and pollution, some types of whales are in danger of becoming extinct.

See also DOLPHINS

wheat 253

Look at the encyclopedia pages. Then complete the items.

1. What are the guide words on these encyclopedia pages? Circle them,

   and write them on the line. _____

2. According to the guide words, which entry would you be most likely to find on pages 252–253? Circle your answer.
   a. wave
   b. Western Ocean
   c. wheel
   d. wharf

3. What cross-reference is listed at the end of the entry?

   _____

TEKS 4.11 (D) Use multiple text features to gain an overview of the contents of text and to locate information.

Name _____

The **rhyme scheme** of a poem is the pattern of rhymes at the
end of each line. The poem's **meter** is the way that accented
and unaccented syllables are arranged in the poem. You can
think of it as the poem's rhythm.

1. **Read the following limerick by Edward Lear. Circle the rhyming
   words at the end of each line. Then put an *a* next to the first set of
   rhyming words and a *b* next to the second set of rhyming words to
   identify the poem's rhyme scheme.**

   There was an Old Man with a beard, _____

   Who said "It is just as I feared!— _____

   Two Owls and a Hen, _____

   Four Larks and a Wren, _____

   Have all built their nests in my beard!" _____

2. **Read the first line of the poem. How would you describe the meter
   of this line?**

   _____

3. **Now write your own limerick below.**

   _____

   _____

   _____

   _____

   _____

© Macmillan/McGraw-Hill

TEKS 4.4 Explain how the structural elements of poetry relate to form.
4.16 (B) Write poems that convey sensory details using the
conventions of poetry.

Adelina's Whales • Grade 4/Unit 5   **223**

Homographs are words that have the same spelling but different meanings. They may also have different pronunciations. You can use a dictionary to find their meanings and pronunciation.

A. Read the list of homographs and their meanings. Then read the sentences and decide the meaning of the underlined homograph. Write the letter of the correct meaning in the blank next to the sentence.

dove – a. past tense of *dive*   **b.** a kind of bird

fluke – c. part of a whale's tail   **d.** something lucky

1. The whale splashed the surface of the water with its <u>fluke</u>. _____

2. The eagle <u>dove</u> for its prey. _____

3. It was a <u>fluke</u> that my mother won the game. _____

4. The bird watchers saw a mourning <u>dove</u> sitting in a tree. _____

B. Pick another homograph. Write one sentence for each meaning of the word.

5. _____

_____

6. _____

_____

TEKS 3.4 (C) Identify and use homographs.

A. Reading Strategy: Summarize

Summarizing information and ideas from texts will help you understand what you read. Keep the meaning of the text clear. Include information from the text in an order that makes sense. Choose a text that you are reading this week, and answer the questions.

What key ideas or events would you include in a summary of the text?

_____

_____

_____

How would you express the meaning of the text in the summary?

_____

_____

_____

B. Independent Reading Log

Choose something that you would like to read. After reading, complete the reading log. Be sure to paraphrase, or tell the main idea or meaning of the text. Keep the details or events in the proper order. You may use your log to talk to others about what you read.

Genre _____

Title _____

Author _____

This Text Is About _____

_____

TEKS **4.9** Read independently for a sustained period of time and paraphrase what the reading was about, maintaining meaning and logical order. **RC-4 (E)** Summarize information in text, maintaining meaning and logical order.

Adelina's Whales • Grade 4/Unit 5   **225**

Name _____

Listen for the final /ən/ sounds at the end of the
following words:

wood**en**	oft**en**	rais**in**	reas**on**	bac**on**

The /ən/ sounds can be spelled *-en*, *-in*, or *-on*.

bacon	proven	button	eleven	cousin	dozen
women	reason	shaken	listen	common	cotton

**Write a word from the box to complete each sentence. Underline
the letters that represent the /ən/ sounds.**

1. Were there any _____ at the mining camps?

2. Nine plus two is one less than a _____.

3. Do you know the _____ why the computer turned into a
   time machine?

4. Miners fried up lots of _____ for their breakfasts.

5. General stores in San Francisco sold yards of _____ for
   all the clothes the miners would need.

6. My great-grandfather had a _____ who was a gold miner.

7. The earthquake left them feeling very _____ up.

8. I love to _____ to stories about the Gold Rush.

9. Most of the miners could sew a patch or a _____ on
   their clothes.

10. The pigeon is a _____ bird in many cities.

TEKS 3.1 (E) Monitor accuracy in decoding.

Name _____

items   clustered   bidding   glistened   overflowing   sturdy

Use the clues below to complete the vocabulary word puzzle.

Across

2. spilling out of a full container
3. grouped together
4. two or more things in a group

Down

1. sparkled and shined
5. making an offer of money for something
6. strong and well built

TEKS **4.2 (B)** Use the context of the sentence to determine the meaning of unfamiliar words.

Name _____

When you read a story, look for the **problem** that the main character has. It may influence all the events that follow. Notice the steps the character takes to find the **solution** to the problem.

Read the passage and each question. Underline the answer in the passage. Then write the answers below.

Ding! Ding! Ding! Marta heard the bell of the ice-cream truck. It was the hottest week of the year, and she felt like she was going to melt. Marta wanted an orange ice pop—she could almost taste it. She counted the money in her pocket: 26 cents. Ice pops cost $1.50. She did not have enough money. Marta remembered that her brother owed her $2.00. She knocked on his bedroom door, but he wasn't home.

Then Marta got an idea. She went to the kitchen and found an ice-cube tray. Carefully, she poured some orange juice into the tray. She covered the tray with plastic wrap and stuck a toothpick into each square. Then she put the tray in the freezer and waited. In a couple of hours, she checked the freezer. She had twelve orange ice pops—enough to last all week.

1. Who is the main character? _____

2. What is the problem? _____

_____

3. What is the first thing Marta does to solve her problem? _____

_____

4. How does Marta solve her problem? _____

_____

5. What might happen next? _____

© Macmillan/McGraw-Hill

TEKS 4.6 (A) Sequence and summarize the plot's main events and explain their influence on future events.

Name _____

As you read *Leah's Pony*, fill in the Problem and Solution Chart.

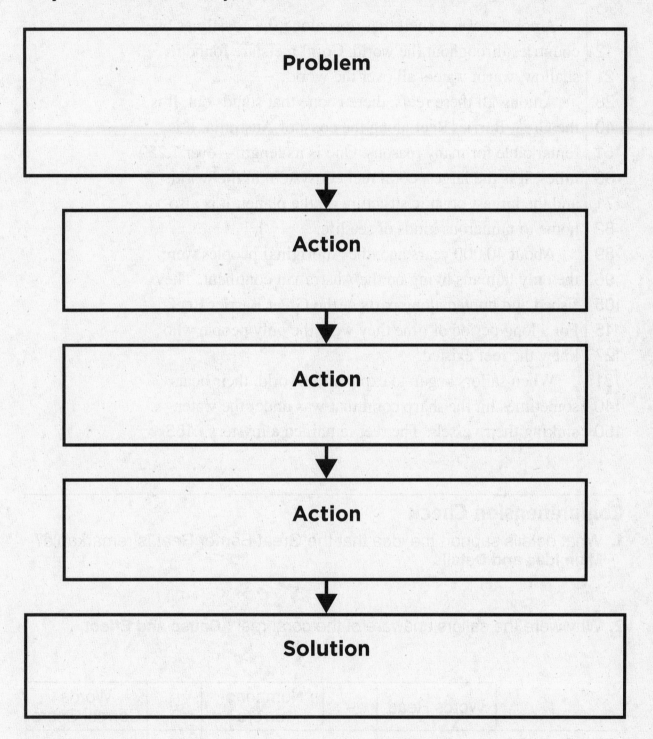

How does the information you wrote in the Problem and Solution Chart help you understand *Leah's Pony*?

TEKS **4.6 (A)** Sequence and summarize the plot's main events and explain their influence on future events.

Name _____

As I read, I will pause at commas and end punctuation.

	A coral reef is a shelf that runs along the coastlines of
12	countries throughout the world. Coral reefs are found in
21	shallow, warm waters all over the world.
28	Among all these reefs, there is one that stands out. It is
40	the Great Barrier Reef along the coast of Australia. It is
51	remarkable for many reasons. One is its length—over 1,250
60	miles. It is the largest coral reef ecosystem in the world,
71	and the largest organic structure on the planet. It is also
82	home to numerous kinds of sea life.
89	About 40,000 years ago, the Aboriginal peoples were
96	the only humans living on the Australian continent. They
105	fished and hunted along parts of the Great Barrier Reef.
115	For a long period of time they were the only people who
127	knew the reef existed.
131	When sailors began to explore the world, their boats
140	sometimes hit the sharp coral that was under the water,
150	sinking their vessels. The reef remained a mystery. 158

Comprehension Check

1. What details support the idea that the Great Barrier Reef is remarkable?
Main Idea and Details

2. Why were the sailors unaware of the coral reef? **Cause and Effect**

	Words Read	–	Number of Errors	=	Words Correct Score
First Read		–		=	
Second Read		–		=	

TEKS **4.1** Read aloud grade-level stories with fluency and comprehension.

The **narrator** is the person who tells the story. Sometimes the narrator is a character in the story and uses the pronoun *I* to tell the story. This type of narrator tells the story from a **first-person** point of view. Sometimes the narrator is not a character in the story and refers to the characters by name or as *he* or *she*. This type of narrator tells the story from a **third-person** point of view.

Read each passage. Then answer the questions below.

Matt jumped into the boat and shouted, "Let's go!" Uncle Josh tossed him a life jacket. "Not just yet," Uncle Josh said. "Let's check our gear first to make sure that we're ready."

Matt was definitely ready. He had been waiting all winter to visit his uncle in Corpus Christi. Now that it was finally warm, they were going fishing. Matt had never been fishing in the ocean before.

Uncle Josh tested the fishing poles and then chose one for Matt. Matt smiled as he took it. He could almost feel the tug of his first fish on the line.

• What is the point of view of this passage? How do you know?

_____

_____

"Let's go!" I shouted to my Uncle Josh when I got to the boat. He handed me a life jacket and told me that we weren't quite ready yet. He explained that we had to check our gear first. He checked the fishing poles. I couldn't wait for him to pick one out for me. I've been waiting all winter to come to Corpus Christi to go fishing. It's my first time to fish in the ocean.

Uncle Josh handed me a fishing pole. It was heavier than I expected it to be. I imagined what it would be like when I got the first bite. I could almost feel it.

• What is the point of view of this passage? How do you know?

_____

_____

TEKS **4.6 (C)** Identify whether the narrator or speaker of a story is first or third person.

Name _____

A **compass rose** shows north, south, east, and west. The **map key**, or **legend**, explains the symbols on the map.

Use the map to answer each question.

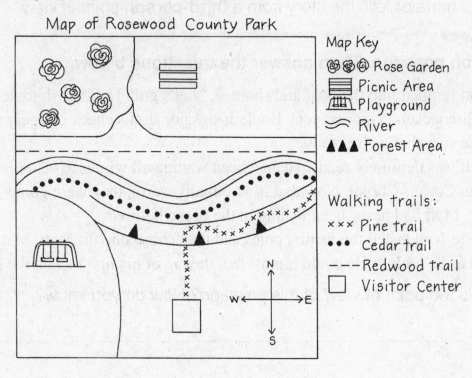

Map of Rosewood County Park

Map Key
🌹🌹🌹 Rose Garden
▤ Picnic Area
♨ Playground
〰 River
▲▲▲ Forest Area

Walking trails:
××× Pine trail
••• Cedar trail
--- Redwood trail
□ Visitor Center

1. The picnic area is to the east of _____.

2. Which trail would you take to walk through the forest area?

   _____

3. Can you take the Cedar trail to get to the Redwood trail? Explain.

   _____

4. It is possible to get from the Visitor Center to the Rose Garden. What is

   missing from the map? _____

TEKS 4.13 (B) Explain factual information presented graphically.

Practice

Name _____

> A **dictionary** can help you find the meanings, pronunciations, and syllabication of **unfamiliar words**.

Look at this dictionary entry for an unfamiliar word. Use the definition and sample sentence to help answer the questions that follow.

> **av•id** (av´id) *adjective.* **1.** very eager. *She is an* avid *reader.*

1. What does *avid* mean, in your own words?

_____

2. What is the pronunciation of *avid*?

_____

3. Use *avid* in another sentence.

_____

4. How would you find the meaning of the word *incognito*?

_____

5. Use a dictionary. Write the meaning of *incognito* below.

_____

6. Use a dictionary. Write the number of syllables in *incognito* below.

_____

© Macmillan/McGraw-Hill

TEKS **4.2 (E)** Use a dictionary to determine the meanings, syllabication, and pronunciation of unknown words.

Name _____

A. Reading Strategy: Make Connections

You can make connections between informational texts and literary texts that are alike in some way. Texts that give facts about something, explain something, or tell how to do something are informational. Stories, poems, plays, biographies, and autobiographies are literary. Choose a text that you are reading this week. Complete the chart by connecting texts. Give details to support your connections.

	Informational Text	**Literary Text**
Main Idea/Theme		
Author's Purpose		

Connections Between the Texts

_____

_____

_____

_____

B. Independent Reading Log

Choose something that you would like to read. After reading, complete the reading log. Be sure to paraphrase, or tell the main idea or meaning of the text. Keep the details or events in the proper order. You may use your log to talk to others about what you read.

Genre _____

Title _____

Author _____

This Text Is About _____

_____

© Macmillan/McGraw-Hill

TEKS **4.9** Read independently for a sustained period of time and paraphrase what the reading was about, maintaining meaning and logical order. **RC-4 (F)** Make connections between literary and informational texts with similar ideas and provide textual evidence.

Homophones are words that sound the same but are spelled differently and have different meanings. The words *right* and *write* are homophones.

　　　right = correct　　　write = make marks on paper

Fill in each blank with the correct homophone.

1. **tale / tail**　　He told a _____ about a lion that lost its

　　_____.

2. **patience / patients**　　The doctor encouraged his _____

　　to have more _____ while they waited to see him.

3. **dough / doe**　　The _____ and her fawns ate the

　　_____ that the baker left on the window sill.

4. **wade / weighed**　　She tried to _____ across the river

　　wearing a backpack that _____ 90 pounds.

5. **bolder / boulder**　　The skier grew _____ after he

　　jumped over the _____.

6. **plain / plane**　　We flew in a _____ over the

　　_____ where the buffalo roamed.

7. **week / weak**　　I felt _____ for a _____.

8. **aloud / allowed**　　"There are no photos _____," the

　　guide said _____.

Name _____

| annoyed | circular | outstretched |
| conducted | reference | disappointment |

A. Draw a line to match the vocabulary word to its meaning.

1. reference

2. disappointment

3. annoyed

4. circular

5. outstretched

6. conducted

a. reaching out

b. led

c. round, like a circle

d. upset

e. the feeling when something doesn't happen the way you hoped it would

f. a source of reliable information

B. Write a paragraph or two using as many of the vocabulary words as possible.

_____

_____

_____

_____

_____

_____

_____

_____

_____

TEKS **4.2 (B)** Use the context of the sentence to determine the meaning of unfamiliar words.

Name _____

A **cause** is what makes something happen. If you can answer the question "Why did that happen?", then you know the cause.

What happens as a result of the cause is the **effect**. If you can answer the question "What happened?", then you know the effect.

Read the passage below. As you read, think about causes and effects. Then answer the questions.

Sam Brannan was a merchant in San Francisco. When he heard that gold had been found near the American River, he knew just what to do. He bought up every pickax, shovel, and pan in the entire city. Then he ran through the streets of San Francisco spreading the news about the discovery of gold.

Because Brannan was the only merchant who had tools to sell, he could charge as much as he wanted. Prospectors were willing to spend $15.00 for a pan that was worth only 60 cents. It wasn't long before Brannan became one of the richest men in California—without ever panning for gold!

1. What caused Sam Brannan to buy up all the mining tools?

_____

2. What was the effect of Brannan's spreading the news about gold?

_____

3. What caused miners to pay $15.00 for a 60-cent pan? _____

_____

4. What was the effect of so many prospectors buying Brannan's tools?

_____

TEKS 4.6 (A) Explain the plot's main events' influence on future events.

Name _____

As you read *The Gold Rush Game*, fill in the Cause and Effect Chart.

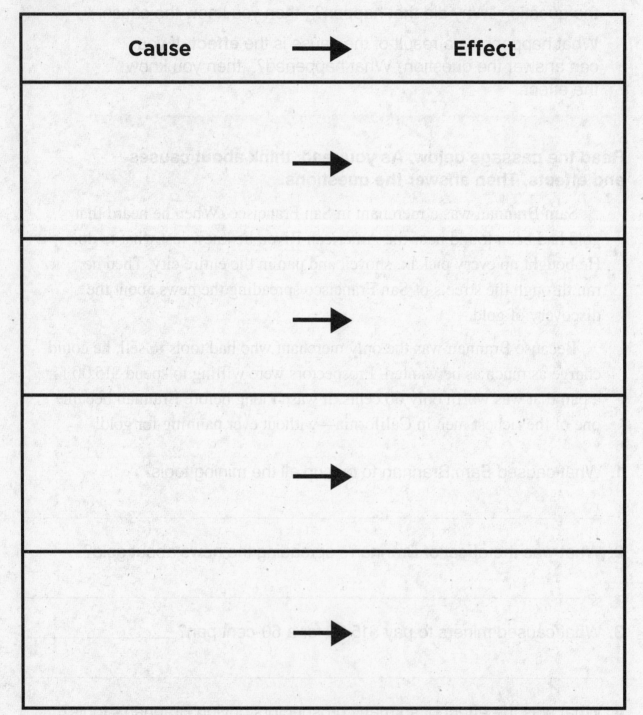

Cause	➡	Effect
	➡	
	➡	
	➡	
	➡	

How does the information you wrote in the Cause and Effect Chart help you to analyze the story structure of *The Gold Rush Game*?

TEKS 4.6 (A) Explain the plot's main events' influence on future events.

As I read, I will pay attention to my intonation and expression.

	In the early 1800s, the United States needed room to grow.
10	Most people lived in the East. The cities were crowded. New land
22	was expensive. Young families couldn't afford to buy farms.
31	Then the United States government purchased land from
39	France. The government also acquired land from Mexico. Soon the
49	country stretched all the way to the Pacific Ocean. People looked
60	to the setting sun with outstretched arms and said, "Go west!"
71	Settlers rode in wagons or on horses. They followed long, dusty
82	trails across hot plains for thousands of miles. There was no shelter.
94	People slept in tents on the ground. They had to watch out for wild
108	animals like wolves and snakes. The trip west could take months.
119	Then a railroad was built that stretched from the East Coast
130	almost to the West Coast. The railroad made travel faster. More
141	people poured into the new lands. The settlers quickly built small
152	towns where the farming, fishing, and mining were good. 161

Comprehension Check

1. What was life like in the East in the 1800s? **Main Idea and Details**

2. What enabled people to move west? **Cause and Effect**

	Words Read	–	Number of Errors	=	Words Correct Score
First Read		–		=	
Second Read		–		=	

© Macmillan/McGraw-Hill

TEKS 4.1 Read aloud grade-level stories with fluency and comprehension.

The Gold Rush Game
Grade 4/Unit 6   **239**

Name _____

Suffixes are word endings that change the meaning of a base word.

The suffixes **-y** and **-ful** mean "full of."

        dirty = full of dirt   joyful = full of joy

The suffix **-ly** *means* "in a certain way."

        nicely = in a nice way

The suffix **-less** *means* "without."

        breathless = without breath

The suffix **-ness** means "the state of being."

        sickness = the state of being sick

Circle the suffix in each word. Then circle the correct meaning of the word.

1. cloudy

   a. full of clouds   **b.** without clouds   **c.** in a clouded way

2. suddenly

   a. full of sudden   **b.** the opposite of sudden   **c.** in a sudden way

3. powerful

   a. without power   **b.** the state of being powered by   **c.** full of power

4. shoeless

   a. full of shoes   **b.** without shoes   **c.** the state of having shoes

5. kindness

   a. the state of being kind   **b.** full of kind   **c.** without any kind

6. loudly

   a. without loud   **b.** full of loud   **c.** in a loud way

A. Choose a word in the box to replace the underlined word or words in each sentence.

technique	foolishness	inspire
evaporate	magnify	annual

1. Lucky for him, Bentley's mother never said, "Stop this <u>silliness</u>! Come in out of the storm at once!" _____

2. Bentley had to develop a special <u>method</u> to photograph snowflakes.

_____

3. The newspaper held an <u>occurring-every-year</u> photo contest.

_____

4. Bentley had to work fast to make sure a snowflake didn't <u>dry up</u>. _____

B. Use each word correctly in a sentence.

5. magnify _____

_____

6. inspire _____

_____

TEKS **4.2 (B)** Use the context of the sentence to determine the meaning of unfamiliar words.

Name _____

> To **draw a conclusion**, use information from the selection and
> your own prior experience connected to the reading selection.

**Read the passage. Then read the conclusions. Support each one
with evidence from the text.**

My science project was due on Wednesday, but things had not gone as
planned. I was trying to train my dog, Snowball, not to bark when someone
came through the door. I had thought that giving Snowball a treat when she
stopped barking would teach her to sit quietly. I'd repeated the procedure
each day for two weeks and recorded the results. Snowball was still barking.

I talked to my teacher, Mrs. Gomez, about my problem. "Hmm," she said.
"From what you've written in your notebook, it looks like the two times when
Snowball did sit quietly, you also used a firm voice and then patted her head."
"You're right!" I exclaimed. "I know exactly what to do."

On Wednesday, the students in Mrs. Gomez's class turned in their reports. I
was last. "Thanks for your help, Mrs. Gomez," I said. "I guess in science,
just like everything else, it's really important to keep on trying."

1. The author's dog Snowball sometimes misbehaves. _____

_____

2. The author would like to improve Snowball's behavior. _____

_____

_____

3. The author's experiment fails. _____

_____

4. The author is concerned about the science experiment. _____

_____

TEKS 5.7 Identify the literary language and devices used in biographies
and autobiographies, including how authors present major events in a
person's life.

Snowflake Bentley • Grade 4/Unit 6 **255**

© Macmillan/McGraw-Hill

As you read *Snowflake Bentley*, fill in the Conclusions Chart.

Text Clues	Conclusion

How does the information you wrote in your Conclusions Chart help
you answer your questions about *Snowflake Bentley*?

© Macmillan/McGraw-Hill

TEKS **5.7** Identify the literary language and devices used in biographies
and autobiographies, including how authors present major events in a
person's life.

As I read, I will focus on reading accurately.

	Tornadoes begin with warm, humid air. Humid air is air
10	that holds a lot of moisture. This humid air meets up with
22	colder air. As the air masses come together, the warm air
33	rises. As the warm air moves upward, it holds more and
44	more moisture. Huge, dark clouds called thunderheads begin
52	to develop. These clouds can spread as wide as 100 miles
62	(161 km) across the sky. There is so much moisture in the
73	clouds that it can't just **evaporate** into the air. So it falls as
86	rain. The thunderheads produce giant storms with thunder
94	and lightning. These storms are called supercells.
101	Winds high up in the storm clouds blow faster than the
112	winds lower down. The winds also blow in different
121	directions. This causes the air to spin. Then, as the winds
132	spin, they form a long funnel cloud. However, one last
142	thing needs to happen for the funnel cloud to become a
153	tornado. It needs to touch the ground. 160

Comprehension Check

1. Describe the conditions needed to form a thunderhead. **Main Idea and Details**

2. What is the author's purpose? **Author's Purpose**

	Words Read	−	Number of Errors	=	Words Correct Score
First Read		−		=	
Second Read		−		=	

© Macmillan/McGraw-Hill

TEKS 4.1 Read aloud grade-level stories with fluency and comprehension.

Snowflake Bentley • **Grade 4/Unit 6** **257**

Authors use **sensory language** to create **imagery**, or pictures in the reader's mind. Sensory language helps readers see, hear, smell, taste, or feel something. A **metaphor** is a figure of speech in which two very different objects or ideas are said to be alike. **Similes** also compare two different things, usually by using the words *like* or *as*.

Read each haiku. Answer the questions that follow.

Children on the beach
Moving back and forth like crabs
Playing in the sand

1. Circle the simile in this haiku. What two things are being compared?

_____

The leaves are feathers
Floating, floating, down, down, down
Red, orange, and brown

2. Circle the metaphor in this haiku. What two things are being compared?

_____

3. What words help you see the leaves as they fall to the ground?

_____

TEKS 4.8 Identify the author's use of similes and metaphors to produce imagery.

> **Imagery** is the use of sensory language to create a picture in the reader's mind. **Metaphor** is the comparison of two different things without the use of *like* or *as*.

Read each haiku and answer the questions that follow.

This light rain falling
Tickles my skin like feathers.
A hot bath calls me.

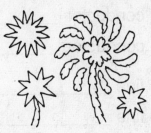

1. What picture comes to mind as you read this haiku?

_____

_____

2. Can a hot bath really call someone? What does this mean?

_____

_____

Sun after gray days—
Bright Fourth of July fireworks—
Bursts forth bright with joy.

3. What is the sun compared to? _____

4. What metaphor is used in the poem? How can you tell?

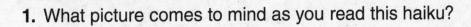

_____

A summer hailstorm—
Daisies burrow underground.
They're not meant for ice!

5. What words in this haiku describe something that could not happen?

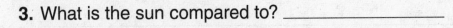

_____

TEKS 4.8 Identify the author's use of metaphors to produce imagery.

Snowflake Bentley • Grade 4/Unit 6   **259**

Multiple-meaning words have more than one meaning. You can use the dictionary to find the meanings, and then use context clues to choose the correct meaning being used in a sentence.

Each of the following words has more than one meaning. Use a dictionary to find the meanings. Write a sentence for each meaning of the word.

1. content _____

   content _____

2. paddle _____

   paddle _____

3. object _____

   object _____

4. conductor _____

   conductor _____

5. fine _____

   fine _____

6. stand _____

   stand _____

© Macmillan/McGraw-Hill

TEKS **4.2 (B)** Use the context of the sentence to determine the meaning of multiple meaning words.
4.2 (E) Use a dictionary to determine the meanings of unknown words.

A. Reading Strategy: Make Connections

You can make connections between informational texts and literary texts that are alike in some way. Texts that give facts about something, explain something, or tell how to do something are informational. Stories, poems, plays, biographies, and autobiographies are literary. Choose a text that you are reading this week. Complete the activity by connecting texts. Give details to support your connections.

Freewrite for a few minutes about ideas from the text that you are reading.

Freewrite for a few minutes about ideas from a text that reminds you of what you are reading.

Use your freewriting to make connections between the texts. Concentrate on making connections about main idea/theme, author's purpose, or author's perspective. Also, give details from the texts to support your connections.

B. Independent Reading Log

Choose something that you would like to read. After reading, complete the reading log. Be sure to paraphrase, or tell the main idea or meaning of the text. Keep the details or events in the proper order. You may use your log to talk to others about what you read.

Genre _____

Title _____

Author _____

This Text Is About _____

_____

TEKS 4.9 Read independently for a sustained period of time and paraphrase what the reading was about, maintaining meaning and logical order. **RC-4 (F)** Make connections between literary and informational texts with similar ideas and provide textual evidence.

Snowflake Bentley • Grade 4/Unit 6   **261**

A **prefix** is a word part that can be added to the beginning of a base word. A prefix changes the meaning of the word. The prefixes **dis-**, **non-**, and **un-** mean "the opposite of" or "without." The prefix **mis-** means "badly" or "incorrectly."

A. Underline the prefix in the following words. Then write the meaning of the word.

1. unusual _____

2. discontent _____

3. misread _____

4. nonsense _____

5. unafraid _____

A **suffix** is a word part that can be added to the end of a base word. Adding a suffix changes the meaning of the base word.
-y and **-ful** mean "full of"   **-ly** means "in a certain way"
-less means "without"   **-ness** means "the state of being"

B. Circle the suffix in each word. Then write the meaning of the word.

6. joyful _____

7. sadness _____

8. quietly _____

9. toothless _____

10. speedy _____

© Macmillan/McGraw-Hill

TEKS 3.1 (E) Monitor accuracy in decoding.

| hilarious | dizzy | nowadays |
| came in handy | mischief | independence |

Fill in the sentences below with words from the box. Then use the words in the blanks to complete the puzzle.

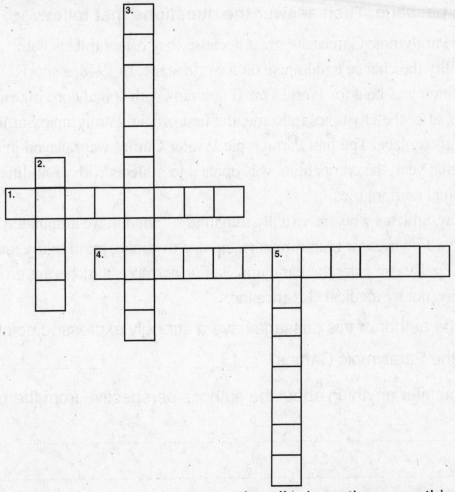

1. I never get into _____ when I'm inventing something!

2. But when success goes to my head, I feel _____!

3. My invention _____ for senior citizens who live alone.

4. It will let them keep their _____.

5. All I do _____ is come up with bright ideas!

TEKS 4.2 (B) Use the context of the sentence to determine the meaning of unfamiliar words.

An **author's perspective** is his or her point of view. It may include the author's attitudes and opinions about a subject. The words *best*, *worst*, *should*, and *ought to* are often used to signal the author's opinion.

Read the passage. Then answer the questions that follow.

The Paralympic Games are great because they offer athletes with a disability the chance to compete on a world stage. In 1948, a sports competition was held for World War II veterans with spinal cord injuries. In 1960, after the Olympics in Rome, the first official Paralympic Summer Games took place. The first Paralympic Winter Games were played in 1976, and in that year, the competition was opened to athletes with disabilities other than spinal cord injuries.

Today, athletes who are visually impaired or blind, have amputated limbs, spinal cord injuries, or motor impairment due to stroke, brain injury, or cerebral palsy can enter the Paralympics. Furthermore, athletes are grouped by ability, not by medical classification.

1. Does the author of this passage have a strongly expressed point of view about the Paralympic Games? _____

2. Can you infer anything about the author's perspective from the passage?

_____

_____

3. What word from the passage signals that the author is expressing an opinion? _____

4. What type of information could the author add to the passage to express a clearer perspective on the Paralympic Games?

_____

_____

TEKS 4.12 (A) Explain how an author uses language to present information to influence what the reader thinks or does.

Name _____

As you read *How Ben Franklin Stole the Lightning*, fill in the Author's Perspective Map.

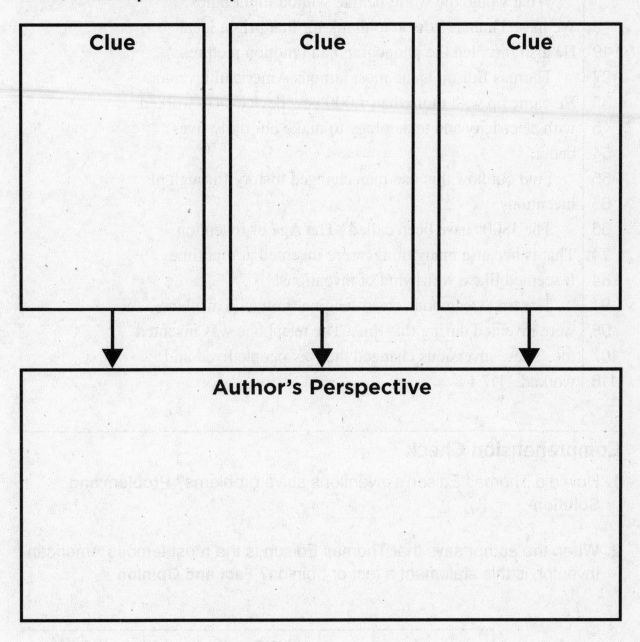

| Clue | Clue | Clue |

Author's Perspective

How does the information you wrote in the Author's Perspective Map help you to answer your questions about *How Ben Franklin Stole the Lightning*?

© Macmillan/McGraw-Hill

TEKS 4.12 (A) Explain how an author uses language to present information to influence what the reader thinks or does.

How Ben Franklin Stole the
Lightning • Grade 4/Unit 6

265

As I read, I will pay attention to my reading rate and accuracy.

	What would the world be like without light bulbs?
9	We have Thomas Edison to thank for that bright idea!
19	He also invented the phonograph and motion pictures.
27	Thomas Edison is the most famous American inventor.
35	He came up with more than 1,000 new devices. He worked
45	with electricity and technology to make our daily lives
54	better.
55	Find out how this one man changed history through his
65	inventions.
66	The 1800s have been called "The Age of Invention."
74	That is because many things were invented at that time.
84	It seemed like a whirlwind of inventions!
91	The first steamboat, steam-engine train, and airplane
98	were invented during this time. The telephone was invented
107	too. These inventions changed the way people lived and
116	worked. 117

Comprehension Check

1. How did Thomas Edison's inventions solve problems? **Problem and Solution**

2. When the author says that Thomas Edison is the most famous American inventor, is this statement a fact or opinion? **Fact and Opinion**

	Words Read	–	Number of Errors	=	Words Correct Score
First Read		–		=	
Second Read		–		=	

TEKS 4.1 Read aloud grade-level stories with fluency and comprehension.

Directions tell how to do something. They usually include numbered steps to tell the order in which things should be done. Directions can also include an **illustration**, or drawing. A list of **materials** often comes before the steps in the directions.

Read the directions. Then answer the questions.

How to Turn a White Carnation Blue

Materials: jar, water, white carnation, scissors, blue food coloring

1. Have an adult help you trim an inch or so off the bottom of the carnation with scissors. Cut the stem at an angle.

2. Fill the jar halfway with water.

3. Put 20 to 30 drops of blue food coloring in the water.

4. Place the carnation in the jar.

5. Check the flower every few hours. After 24 hours, the food coloring should have reached the white petals and turned your white carnation blue.

← The petals have tiny holes called stomata that release the dye.

Water moves up the stem and into the petals

1. Look at the illustration. How does the water move?

_____

2. What are the tiny holes in carnation petals called? What do they do?

_____

_____

> **Figurative Language** uses words to create mental images.
> **Alliteration** is the repetition of the same consonant sound in a series of words.

Read the poem. Then circle or fill in the correct answer.

The wonderful wheel, which changed the world,
Is as round as a ring and rolls and twirls
For carts and coaches,
Cabbies and kings.
The wonderful wheel—a roll of thunder what bustle it brings!

1. What is this poem about?
   a. a wheel   **b.** a ring

2. Which words in the poem are an example of alliteration?
   a. round, rolls, ring   **b.** twirls and changed

3. Which is figurative language?
   a. carts and coaches   **b.** roll of thunder

4. What are the two reasons why "carts" was placed with "coaches" and

   "cabbies" was placed with "kings"? _____

   _____

   _____

© Macmillan/McGraw-Hill

TEKS **4.8** Identify the author's use of similes and metaphors to produce imagery.

> **Idioms** are phrases that have a meaning different from the
> meaning of each word in them. For example: "pulling my leg".
> This group of words means "to trick or to tease." You can use
> a **dictionary** or context clues to help you understand the
> meaning of an idiom.

1. Read the sentence; then circle the meaning of "out of the blue."

The news came *out of the blue*, so Isaac was shocked.

a. suddenly   **b.** out of the sky

2. Use "out of the blue" in a sentence.

_____

3. Read the sentence; then circle the meaning of "wind up."

The meeting was almost over when Janet said, "Let's *wind up* by
six o'clock."

a. change time on the clock   **b.** finish

4. Use "wind up" in a sentence.

_____

5. Read the sentence; then circle the meaning of "under the weather."

Zachary was rarely sick, so his teacher was surprised to hear that he was
under the weather.

a. lying under a cloud   **b.** feeling sick

6. Use "under the weather" in a sentence.

_____

© Macmillan/McGraw-Hill

TEKS 4.2 (D) Identify the meaning of common idioms.
4.2 (E) Use a dictionary to determine the meanings of unknown words.

How Ben Franklin Stole the
Lightning • **Grade 4/Unit 6**   **269**

A. Reading Strategy: Make Connections

You can make connections between informational texts and literary texts that are alike in some way. Texts that give facts about something, explain something, or tell how to do something are informational. Stories, poems, plays, biographies, and autobiographies are literary. Choose a text that you are reading this week. Complete the chart by connecting texts. Give details to support your connections.

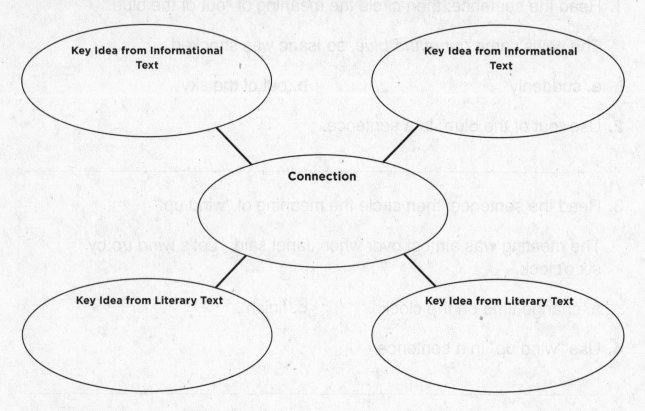

B. Independent Reading Log

Choose something that you would like to read. After reading, complete the reading log. Be sure to paraphrase, or tell the main idea or meaning of the text. Keep the details or events in the proper order. You may use your log to talk to others about what you read.

Genre _____

Title _____ Author _____

This Text Is About _____

TEKS **4.9** Read independently for a sustained period of time and paraphrase what the reading was about, maintaining meaning and logical order. **RC-4 (F)** Make connections between literary and informational texts with similar ideas and provide textual evidence.

Contents

Show What You Know

Use "A Walk on the Beach" (pp. 126–127) to answer questions 1–5.

1 When Tony first arrives at his cousin's house, he thinks that —

A the ocean is less interesting than the desert

B Jenny isn't very happy to see him

C every creature he sees is poisonous

D Jenny is jealous because he is always right

2 At the beach, Jenny makes fun of Tony because he —

F does not know how plants can grow on sand

G is too scared to get out of the car

H sees some dolphins and calls them sharks

J thinks that a harmless spider is a tarantula

3 What does the word <u>thrilled</u> mean on page 127?

A Excited

B Scared

C Interested

D Curious

4 How have Jenny and Tony changed by the end of the story?

F Jenny likes to be outdoors, but Tony likes to be indoors.

G They promise always to be honest with each other.

H Jenny is right all the time, and Tony always is wrong.

J Each of them learns to appreciate where the other comes from.

© Macmillan/McGraw-Hill

Page 1

GO ON ➤

Student Name _____

5 How are Jenny and Tony alike? Explain your answer and support it with evidence from the story.

_____

_____

_____

_____

_____

_____

_____

_____

_____

TP2   A Walk on the Beach • **Grade 4/Unit 1**   **Show What You Know**

Use "Diamonds for the Taking" (pp. 128–129) to answer questions 1–5.

1 In the section called "Prospecting for Diamonds," the author organizes the information mainly by—

A comparing and contrasting different kinds of prospectors

B discussing the prospecting methods in order of importance

C telling about digging for diamonds in time order

D explaining the effects of different methods of prospecting

2 Look at the map on page 128. What county is north of Herkimer?

F Madison County

G St. Lawrence County

H Fulton County

J Otsego County

3 Look at the map on page 128. Herkimer County is located in what part of New York State?

A Western

B Eastern

C Southern

D Central

4 In the last paragraph on page 128, the word <u>seeped</u> means —

F trapped

G blasted

H leaked

J burned

© Macmillan/McGraw-Hill

Page 1

GO ON ▶

5 How are Herkimer diamonds different from true diamonds? Explain your answer and support it with evidence from the article.

_____

_____

_____

_____

_____

_____

_____

_____

Use "Reading for Mr. Paredo" (pp. 258–259) to answer questions 1–5.

1 What happens before Benito opens the door to Mr. Paredo's room?

A Mr. Paredo stares at Benito.

B A nurse tells Benito to knock louder.

C Benito rummages through his backpack.

D A magazine falls and hits Mr. Paredo.

3 What makes Mr. Paredo smile for the first time?

A Benito offers to read him a magazine.

B He sees Benito's comic book.

C Benito comes to visit him in the hospital.

D He interrupts Benito to ask questions.

2 In paragraph 1, the word <u>quietly</u> means —

F not quiet

G a person who is quiet

H in a quiet way

J very quiet

4 What does the word <u>unprepared</u> mean?

F Very ready

G Ready before

H Not ready

J Ready again

Page 1

GO ON ➤

5 What happens after Benito finishes reading? Explain your answer and support it with evidence from the story.

_____

_____

_____

_____

_____

_____

_____

_____

> **Use "Protect Our Valuable Oceans" (pp. 260–261) to answer questions 1–5.**

1 Look at the web of information from the article.

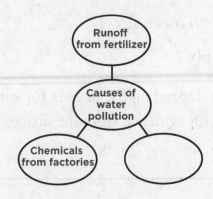

Which information belongs in the empty oval?

A Waste from cruise ships

B Too much oxygen from plants

C Sick and dying animals

D Salt and other minerals

---

2 What is the main idea of the article?

F Fish, seaweed, and shellfish all come from the ocean.

G Oil tankers transport 60% of the oil used by the world.

H We should protect the oceans that are so important to us and our planet.

J Luckily there are things we can do to protect oceans.

3 Look at the chart on page 261. Which ocean has the largest area?

A Indian Ocean

B Pacific Ocean

C Arctic Ocean

D Atlantic Ocean

Page 1

4 Water pollution in the ocean is a big problem because it —

    F kills many sea creatures

    G comes from big cities

    H makes cruise ships go more slowly

    J poisons the oil supply

5 In what ways do people depend on the oceans for survival? Explain your answer and support it with evidence from the article.

_____

_____

_____

_____

_____

_____

STOP

Use "Diary of a Scarecrow's Helper" (pp. 396–397) to answer questions 1–5.

1 What happens before March 15?

   A Jack Patches gets a new pair of eyes.

   B Uncle Jorge builds a new post for Jack Patches.

   C Mr. Collins explains what happened to Jack Patches.

   D A storm breaks the metal pole Jack Patches used to hang on.

2 In the March 22 entry, what does the word <u>redo</u> mean?

   F Do well

   G Do before

   H Do again

   J Not do

3 Mr. Collins did not put Jack Patches back up because he —

   A did not want anyone to get hurt

   B wanted to talk to Jack's owner first

   C did not like the way Jack looked

   D needed more space for new plants

4 The reader can tell that the writer of this diary plans to —

   F sell Jack Patches to someone else

   G grow vegetables in the community garden

   H ask Mr. Collins for a new shirt

   J put the new Jack Patches on the garbage pile

Page 1

GO ON ➡

5 How is Jack Patches improved by March 23? Explain your answer and support it with evidence from the diary.

_____

_____

_____

_____

_____

_____

> ## Use "Silent Spring No Longer: Rachel Carson" (pp. 398–399) to answer questions 1–5.

1 Look at the chart below.

Fact		Opinion	
Tests showed that Carson was right.	The chemicals made the birds' eggs very frail.	Carson's writing was wonderful and made the sea come alive.	

Which of the following belongs in the empty rectangle?

A *Chemicals were harming the environment and causing birds to die out.*

B *President John F. Kennedy called for testing of chemicals used as pesticides.*

C *Pesticides were harming the environment and causing birds to die out.*

D *Now each spring you can hear these wonderful birds singing in the trees.*

2 Look at the line graph on page 399. In which year was the population of bald eagles smallest?

F 1963

G 1974

H 1982

J 1996

3 Look at the line graph on page 399. What happened between 1988 and 1992?

A The U.S. government banned DDT.

B Birds began eating new kinds of insects.

C The population of bald eagles grew quickly.

D Americans decided to help the bald eagle.

© Macmillan/McGraw-Hill

Page 1

4 In the third paragraph, the word <u>unwanted</u> means —

   F wanted again

   G not wanted

   H wanted before

   J very wanted

5 What is one fact that Rachel Carson wrote about in *Silent Spring*? Explain your answer and support it with evidence from the article.

_____

_____

_____

_____

_____

_____

Page 2

STOP

Use "Mouse and Crow" (pp. 532–533) to answer questions 1–5.

1 The reader can conclude that Crow —

  A is jealous of Mouse and wants her collection

  B wants to teach Mouse how to fly

  C recognizes precious things when he sees them

  D is Mouse's trusted friend

2 To Mouse, the sky seemed limitless. What does the word limitless mean?

  F Causing fear

  G Very blue

  H Without end

  J Not high

3 What problem does Mouse have after she flies with Crow?

  A She needs to wash her green crystal.

  B She cannot find her shiny bottle caps.

  C She boasts too often about her crystals.

  D She cannot get home without Crow's help.

4 What is an important message in this story?

  F Gems are the most beautiful things you can collect.

  G Be careful when sharing information with strangers.

  H Friends will always help you when you are in trouble.

  J You should tell the truth even if it will get you into trouble.

Page 1

GO ON

5 What lesson does Mouse learn? Explain your answer and support it with evidence from the story.

_____

_____

_____

_____

_____

_____

Use "How to Change a Flat Tire on a Bike" (pp. 534–535) to answer questions 1–5.

1 Use the information in the chart to answer the question.

How to Change a Bicycle Tube
1. Remove old tube
2. Check tire and remove objects
3. _____
4. Put new tube into old tire

Which of the following belongs on the third line?

A Put wheel back on bicycle frame

B Release all air from tire

C Put a little air in tube

D Use lever to remove tire

---

2 Which section of the article describes how to put the tire back onto the wheel?

F Section 2

G Section 3

H Section 4

J Section 5

3 In the second paragraph, what does the word <u>manual</u> mean?

A Having two or more parts

B A handbook of instructions

C Needing special tools

D A vehicle with two wheels

Page 1

GO ON ▶

4 The author organizes information in this article by —

    F giving a series of steps

    G stating a cause and its effects

    H telling how things are alike and different

    J making an argument and giving reasons to support it

5 What are tire levers used for? Explain your answer and support it with details from the article.

_____

_____

_____

_____

_____

_____

_____

STOP

Use "Tiger's Teacher" (pp. 664-665) and "Turtle Tricks the Trickster" (pp. 666–667) to answer questions 1-5.

---

1 What is Tiger's main problem?

   A He is not very strong or brave.

   B He does not know how to climb trees.

   C He has a hard time catching animals.

   D He lives at the top of a mountain.

2 Which sentence uses the word <u>dove</u> in the same way it is used in the last paragraph?

   F The <u>dove</u> flew away from the cat.

   G The girl was as kind and gentle as a <u>dove</u>.

   H Both children <u>dove</u> towards the last donut.

   J The <u>dove</u> has long been a symbol of peace.

3 What happens just after Cat finishes teaching Tiger?

   A Cat feels sorry for Tiger.

   B Tiger tries to catch Cat.

   C Cat agrees to help Tiger.

   D Tiger promises not to harm Cat.

4 Who is telling "Tiger's Teacher"?

   F Tiger

   G Cat

   H A first-person narrator

   J A third-person narrator

Page 1

GO ON ➡

5 How are Cat and Turtle similar? Explain your answer and support it with evidence from the story.

_____

_____

_____

_____

_____

_____

_____

> **Use "Tiger's Teacher" (pp. 664-665) and "Turtle Tricks the Trickster" (pp. 666-667) to answer questions 1-5.**

1 Use the diagram to answer the question below.

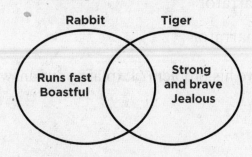

Rabbit   Tiger

Runs fast
Boastful

Strong
and brave
Jealous

Which idea belongs in the middle space?

A Laughs a lot

B Gets help from family

C Gets tricked

D Wears white feather

2 Before Rabbit agrees to race, he —

F puts on a white feather

G gathers his family

H runs up the first hill

J tells tales about himself

3 Which words in the first paragraph of "Turtle Tricks the Trickster" help the reader know what <u>bank</u> means?

A *One morning*

B *of the brook*

C *in the sunshine*

D *smart and wonderful*

© Macmillan/McGraw-Hill

Page 1

GO ON ▶

4 Who is telling "Turtle Tricks the Trickster"?

   F Rabbit

   G Turtle

   H A first-person narrator

   J A third-person narrator

5 How does Turtle solve his problem? Explain your answer and support it with details from the story.

_____

_____

_____

_____

_____

_____

STOP

Use "Pitch for Fish" (pp. 802–803) to answer questions 1–5.

1 Why are Alison, Rosa, and Javier having a meeting?

   A to help children choose the right pets

   B to decide what to do for the school fair

   C to make a plan to save some fish

   D to work together to finish their homework

2 What is Rosa's problem in the story?

   F Javier does not agree with her.

   G She does not know how to paint.

   H Alison wants to be her friend.

   J She does not like Alison's plan.

3 In the sixth paragraph, the phrase "lend a hand" means —

   A raise one's hand

   B give money

   C help someone

   D shake hands

4 When Rosa interrupts Alison, she —

   F makes Alison angry

   G apologizes to Alison

   H makes Javier laugh

   J agrees with Javier

5 How do the students solve their problem? Explain your answer and support it with evidence from the story.

_____

_____

_____

_____

_____

_____

_____

STOP

Use "Caves: Mysterious Underground Worlds" (pp. 804–805) to answer questions 1–5.

---

1 Use the diagram to answer the question below.

Fact	Opinion
There are about 40,000 caves in the United States.	

Which idea from the article belongs in the empty box?

A *There are four basic types of caves.*

B *Choose your clothing carefully.*

C *Caves can be exciting places to explore.*

D *There is no natural light in a cave.*

---

2 Which sentence from the article shows how solution caves are formed?

F *When the lava in the center drains, it creates a cave.*

G *The constant flow of water dissolves and wears away the rock.*

H *They are often so deep below the ground that natural light does not reach inside.*

J *Caves are natural spaces, like rooms, that have opening you can reach from the inside.*

3 Look at the "Travel Journal" on page 805. The reader can tell that this journal is an example of a primary source because it —

A includes two sets of dates

B is written by hand

C names two places in Kentucky

D is a first-person account

© Macmillan/McGraw-Hill

Page 1

4 In the "Travel Journal," the phrase "call it a day" means —

    F stop what one is doing

    G make a telephone call

    H visit some nice places

    J choose a name for the day

5 According to the "Travel Journal," what did the writer's family do on June 20–21 and June 27–29? Explain your answer and support it with details from the story.

_____

_____

_____

_____

_____

_____

STOP

Page 2